Automation:
WHAT IT IS,
HOW IT WORKS,
WHO CAN USE IT

GOLLANCZ PRIMERS FOR OUR TIME

Automation:
WHAT IT IS,
HOW IT WORKS,
WHO CAN USE IT

by CARL DREHER

Illustrated by Herb Lebowitz

London · VICTOR GOLLANCZ LTD · *1958*

PRINTED IN GREAT BRITAIN BY
LOWE AND BRYDONE (PRINTERS) LIMITED, LONDON, N.W.10

Contents

Acknowledgments

A LOT OF stuff which doesn't appear textually in a book is there in spirit, so to speak. What did get in, and stayed there, must first have got into the writer's head from somebody or somewhere before it came out as his own. He certainly wasn't born with it. Some of my immediate sources I have mentioned in the appropriate places. In addition, the following companies and individuals helped by furnishing technical literature, copies of speeches, or answers to questions.

American Automatic Typewriter Company, Chicago; American Management Association, New York, and its Third Annual Electronics Conference (1957); American Telephone and Telegraph Company, New York; W. F. & John Barnes Company, Rockford, Illinois; British Information Services, New York; Computer Control Company, Wellesley, Massachusetts; Allen B. Du Mont Laboratories, Inc., Clifton, New Jersey; E. I. Du Pont de Nemours

Acknowledgments

& Company, Wilmington, Delaware: *Fortune* Magazine, New York; General Electric Company (General Purpose Control Department, Bloomington, Illinois, and other departments); GMC Truck & Coach Division, General Motors Corporation, Pontiac, Michigan; Instrument Society of America, Pittsburgh; James R. Irving of the Scientific Apparatus Makers Association, Chicago; P. H. Kirshen of United Merchants and Manufacturers, Inc., New York; Panellit, Inc., Skokie, Illinois, and Albert F. Sperry; Pratt & Whitney Aircraft, East Hartford, Connecticut; Radio Corporation of America, New York; Rockbar Corporation, Mamaroneck, N. Y.; Sahlin Engineering Company, Inc., Troy, Michigan; Third International Automation Exposition (1956), New York; Vapor Recovery Systems Company, Compton, California; Westinghouse Electric Corporation (Motor and Control Division, Buffalo, N. Y., and other departments).

I can best express my appreciation by absolving these organizations and individuals of any responsibility whatsoever for my views, conclusions, and prognostications.

CARL DREHER

Automation:
WHAT IT IS,
HOW IT WORKS,
WHO CAN USE IT

CHAPTER 1

Sooner Than You Think

SOME HOLD that automation will come only gradually because of the large investments involved, the scarcity of qualified engineers, the opposition of labor, uncertainties in the economic outlook, etc. These retarding factors may easily be overrated in particular areas, perhaps even over-all. The movies switched over from silent pictures to talkies in about three years. Automation, of course, takes in far more ground, but the example shows how fast a modern high-pressure transition can move. There are no precedents which really fit: the steam turbine for electric-generator drive, alternating-current power distribution, the dieselization of locomotives, even the advent of the automobile, were all on a smaller technological and social scale. But a general pattern can be discerned. First, a period of apparently insuperable difficulties and disheartening miscarriages; then wavering progress brought up short by a wall of vested interests; then some slight cracks in the wall,

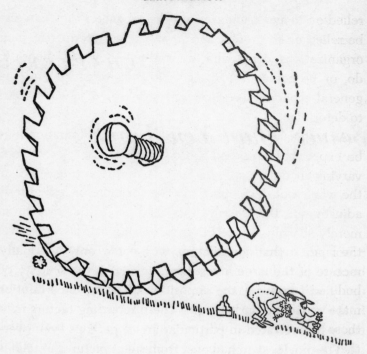

soon followed by larger ones; finally, a breakthrough culminating in a rush to do what everybody else is doing.

The impelling factors in automation are the same as in these earlier cases. The breakthrough has already occurred, and if the technological difficulties are greater, the resources of today's technology are greater also. Electronics, nucleonics, advanced instrumentation, automation are all tied together in what amounts to a new technology, the powers of which most of us as yet scarcely suspect. In any particular application it can advance as rapidly as the top-management echelons may deem desirable. They can be relied on to avoid unnecessary disturbances; they can also be relied on to protect and promote the interests of their organizations, come what may. What they will choose to do, or be compelled to do, in this context, depends on general economic conditions which are not always theirs to determine.

As long as the sun of prosperity shines, automation may be expected to proceed more or less at the present rate, varying in different fields and at different times but on the whole not developing too fast for more or less orderly adjustment. But should the shadow of depression, or merely sharply lowered corporation profits, advance over the land, automation will advance as rapidly. It will be a race to beat falling prices with falling costs. Not everybody will be in a position to automate. Those will automate who have the resources and the hardihood, and from those who have not will be taken away even that which they have. It will be an automation shakeout, and it will hit the smallest hardest.

The gradualist view also fails to take into account the characteristic verve of American business leaders in an era of expansion such as we have experienced since World War II. These top men in the corporate bureaucracies are keenly aware of the perils of being left behind in the technological race—"automate or die," as one of them has put it. He wasn't overdramatizing. In a sober McGraw-Hill magazine, *Factory Management and Maintenance* (September, 1955), Carroll W. Boyce, writing on "What Automation Means to America," forecast the automated future:

"Some companies—and perhaps whole industries—will become economically sick as short-sighted management or far-sighted competitors (and generally a combination of both) put the skids under individual segments of our industrial society." As for individuals, executives, as well as mechanics, will bear the brunt of automation: "New technology is exposing management to ideas that were not dealt with in the textbooks and the classroom of ten or fifteen years ago, much less thirty or forty. The executive who does not keep his ideas modern by constant, aggressive learning from every available source will increasingly often be called on to make decisions on problems he cannot grasp. . . . because something was good or bad in the past doesn't mean it will necessarily be either good or bad in the future."

The perils will be matched by opportunities. Within each organization, policy conflicts will center about the time and pace of automation and careers will be made and unmade by the outcome. Within each industry, and on a national and international scale, the possible rewards of being early and right will loom as large as the penalties of being late and wrong. Some will try to play it safe, but a leader is willing to take the plunge once he is convinced the odds are in his favor; that's one reason he's a leader.

As for money, there are always ample funds for machinery that will lower costs and increase profit margins, or turn out a better and more salable product. In some instances obsolete machinery can be replaced with automatic equipment at no greater cost than conventional equipment. Small companies may encounter difficulty, but many of the big outfits have the necessary funds in their own bank accounts and security portfolios, and those who haven't will be welcome in the money markets for such a laudable purpose. A corporation can't borrow on its labor force, but it can borrow on labor-saving machinery and machinery that will increase plant efficiency in other ways. Moreover, machinery can be written off on income-tax returns, in some cases at a rate that will make dynamic directors even more dynamic.

The other arguments in the negative need not detain us. The world, led by the United States, is on a technological binge. The unions can't stop it and modern union leaders are too smart to try; they will settle for the guaranteed annual wage and suchlike palliatives. As for engineers, the requisite technical talent will be enticed from other technologies and other organizations, possibly leaving these understaffed, but that consideration will weigh no more with the professional seducers of industrial personnel than with their counterparts in the realm of love. The well-rewarded victims will be trained for their new tasks with a speed that will astonish no one who witnessed what was done in similar situations, both in industry and the armed services, in World War II and subsequently.

By all indications, then, both the woes and the wonders of automation will be on us in rapidly increasing measure, and as is the way in such matters, the wonders, though truly wonderful, will not be quite as wonderful as they appeared at a distance. "The future is a door ajar. We stand on the threshold of a golden tomorrow. . . . Automation is a magical key to creation . . . the sky is the limit" (National Association of Manufacturers) might go over at a pep rally of a rather unsophisticated high school, but there is so much to automation that it simply cannot all be pleasant. It may entail some serious derangements of the status quo. But it need not turn into the technological nightmare forecast in some quarters. Since the thing is coming in any case, it would seem sensible to embrace it with ardor—and some caution—and hope for the best in what is neither the best nor the worst of possible worlds.

CHAPTER 2

What Is It?

"AUTOMATION," the word, sprang full-grown from the forehead of Delmar S. Harder, the executive vice president of the Ford Motor Company, who was innocently trying to describe the latest type of assembly-line technique and had no idea of raising a philological monument to himself. John Diebold is said to be a co-begetter of the term, but he doesn't appear to love it as a father should; he quotes Norbert Wiener's characterization of it as "barbarous." At that, Professor Wiener is less repelled than Sir Anthony Eden, who has referred to it as "hideous." Nobody seems to like the word, but everybody uses it.

"Detroit automation," as the Harder variety is called, is advanced mechanization plus electronic control. The underlying reason for automation (there has to be a convincing reason because this type of automation is expensive) is that in the manufacture of, say, an engine block, a great number of cutting, boring, drilling, and other machining operations must be performed, and for each operation the workpiece must be accurately positioned and held in place. These movements may consume as much time and labor as the machining itself. Electronic control may be introduced piecemeal and on a semiautomatic basis, so that a good many men are still around observing signal lights and pushing buttons. Even so, one man may be doing what several men did before. At a later stage, the *transfer machine* combines in one supermachine the tools which perform the successive operations, and moves the workpiece automatically through the entire sequence. The only loading and unloading required is at the beginning and end of the production line embodied in the transfer machine. This stage of automation involves a higher degree of electronic control, and still fewer men.

Detroit automation is obviously important and the transfer machines, some of them as long as a football field, are spectacular exhibits. But automation is much more than a system of production. It is a kind of proto-engineering which gives promise of changing the face of every branch of technology, from business computations to warfare. Nor is it limited to industrial and commercial technology. We shall see that some of the most noteworthy applications are in the field of medicine, and that automation has already made its way into places as unlikely as musical composition. Psychology, epistemology, philosophy cannot remain unaffected. No one has any idea yet of where the boundaries may be—or if there are boundaries.

The electronic computer gives some idea of the amount

of ground automation takes in. Actually, "computer" isn't a very apt name for these devices: some of them do very little computing. A more truly descriptive label is "information- (or data) processing machine." In this light, a television system is a form of computer—it takes in information through microphones and cameras, converts it into electronic impulses, processes it, and reconverts it into picture and sound. However, "computer," being short, will no doubt continue to be used.

The underlying concepts of computers and other automation machinery are those of *communication, information, memory* (associated with *taping*), *programming, open-loop control, closed-loop control,* and *feedback.*

First, *communication:* In automation lingo, when you turn on the light bulb at the head of the stairs by means of a switch at the bottom, you have communicated with the light. Or, in a technical paper on instruments used in connection with blood flow in hospital patients, the author speaks of "the basic problem of communication with the patient's blood stream." These usages seem strange because we are accustomed to thinking of communication in terms of transfer of signals or information between conscious beings. In automation, however, we must also communicate with machines, and machines must communicate with machines. Hence it is necessary to consider measurement, or changes in physical state according to a predictable pattern, as involving communication. Even transportation may be regarded as a form of communication, in direct, physical form instead of by symbols. Communication by speech, reading and writing, etc., is only a special form of communication in the automation sense.

The concepts of *information* and computation have also undergone modifications at the hands of the automationists. One of the most charming and accomplished actresses ever to grace the stage and screen is reputed to have worn

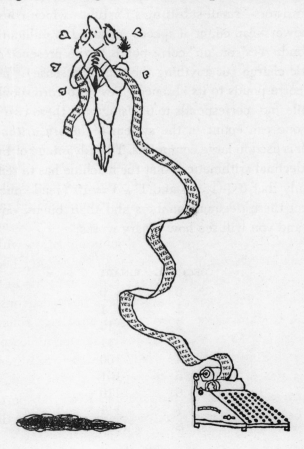

a belt buckle inscribed, "Yes, no, maybe." If Miss Miriam Hopkins had been a digital computer instead of a woman she would have had to drop the "maybe." The common snap switch which turns the electric light on and off is constructed on this either-or principle; it is incapable of in-betweenness or uncertainty. Snap switches would be too large, slow, and clumsy for computation, but electron tubes or transistors—small substitutes for tubes which consume less power—can count at speeds reckoned in millionths of a second. "Yes" or "on" corresponds to the presence of an electric charge (or anything the tube can sense); "no" or "off" corresponds to its absence. "Yes" also corresponds to 1, while "no" corresponds to 0. Using only these two symbols, one can count in the system of *binary arithmetic,* which is used in large computers. The advantage of binary over decimal arithmetic is that the machine has to remember only that $0 + 1 = 1$ and $1 + 1 = 10$ (read "one-0"). Inspect these decimal numbers and their binary equivalents and you will see how binary works:

DECIMAL	BINARY
0	0
1	1
2	10
3	11
4	100
5	101
6	110
7	111
8	1000

What Is It?

DECIMAL	BINARY
9	1001
10	1010
20	10100
40	101000

Zero and 1 are the same in the two systems. From there on, since they are composed of only two building blocks instead of ten, the binary numbers are longer but simpler. In either system, adding a zero multiplies by the base number: $2 \times$ in binary, $10 \times$ in decimal. Addition is the same: you add in one column as long as you can, then shift one column to the left, thereby multiplying by the base number. In decimal your first shift is when you have passed 9, in binary when you have passed 1. You "carry" to the left in exactly the same way, but in binary you necessarily carry oftener.

The computer doesn't care about the length of the numbers: it works so fast the aggregate doesn't matter. What does matter is that aggregates should be composed of only two symbols. The user of the machine doesn't need to know binary. Decimal arithmetic is fed into the machine and the answers are printed out in decimal form. The binary system operates only within the machine and is, so to speak, its private affair.

Computers and other data-processing and control machines also deal in logic: for this they require only three functions, which are called *and, or,* and *not,* and a fourth which is sometimes called "memory" but is essentially a decision mechanism. *And* equipment corresponds to

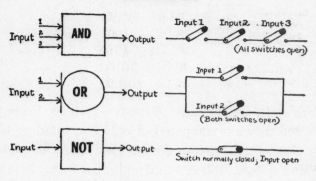

switches (or tubes or other gates) in series. No current can flow unless all the switches are closed. *Or* equipment corresponds to two switches in parallel; if either is closed, current can flow. A *not* device allows current to flow when there is no input; input causes the switch to open. It is therefore an inhibiting device, but, like most inhibitions, it may be overcome.

The Westinghouse Electric Corporation, in some descriptive material concerning its "Cypak" magnetic controls, explains how such a system works. For example, the machine must decide whether a man will smoke after breakfast. At upper left of the system diagram there is an *and* unit with three inputs: cigarette, match, and desire. Unless all three are present, the unit cannot pass current. The man might, however, be a pipe smoker, so we add another *and* unit with four inputs. Brushing aside the kind of fellow who smokes a pipe and a cigarette at the same time, both *and* units feed into an *or* unit. But some men have a prejudice against smoking after breakfast, hence a *not* unit is tied into the circuit to block the output of the

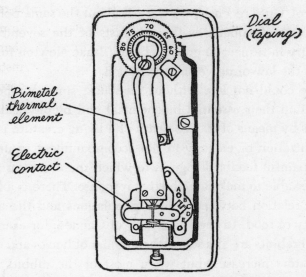

Dial *(taping)*

Bimetal thermal element

Electric contact

ated dial. He is taping the plant—giving it instructions which it then follows without further effort on his part.

This is authentic closed-loop automation. A portion of the product or output—heat energy in this instance—is sent back to the thermostat to enable it to shut down the burner when the desired temperature has been reached. This action is called *feedback*. Feedback is the difference between open-end and closed-loop automation.

This definition of feedback is true as far as it goes, but it is like saying that Napoleon Bonaparte was a short man without hair on his chest. There is much else, of much more significance, to be said about Napoleon—and about feedback. The importance of feedback in nature was not realized for a long time after men began to use it in automatic control. Until recently, we were at about the same point in respect to feedback as the scientists of the seventeenth century in respect to gravity, before Isaac Newton formulated the law of universal gravitation.

We could not live without feedback, since our bodies maintain their essential biochemical and biophysical balances by means of it. The death of a living creature is disorganization or entropy to the accompaniment of urgent and painful feedback signals to which the organism is no longer able to make an effective response. There is a feedback relation between animal populations and the availability of food. In the "fur cycle" of Canada, for example, when rabbits are abundant, the number of lynxes and other predators increases, but when most of the rabbits have been eaten and a lynx can't just go around the corner and pick up a rabbit, the number of lynxes in turn declines. The same theory has been applied to the business cycle, and while it is certainly not a complete explanation, neither is a complete explanation possible without it. Feedback is also a factor in armament races, with each contender basing its standards of adequate war potential on the rising standard of the other.

Feedback is embodied in all personal experience which involves observation or learning. Norbert Wiener defines it as "the property of being able to adjust future conduct by past performance." Albert F. Sperry says, "Feedback is the key to successful activity, whether human or machine; it makes a science of acting from present experience, rather than from some preconceived plan." Both definitions are true. Sperry, who builds control machinery for oil refineries and other plants, stresses the close interplay of immediate physical factors which is essential for control; at the same time he builds past experience into his equipment. There could be no technological progress without feedback.

Feedback also has ethical and romantic applications. Tolstoy remarked that we love people for the good we do them and hate them for the evil: the closed loop brings back to us their happiness or their misery to be reflected —and amplified—in our own feelings. Sexual love is feedback *à deux*. And, as in any feedback system, things can go wrong. Even the relatively simple disorders of feedback in automation are not easily cured.

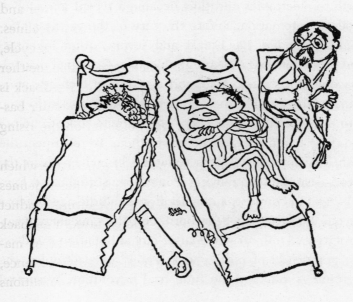

CHAPTER 3

How It Got Here

AUTOMATION has an odd technological history, quite unlike that of radio, for instance. Radio, nee "wireless," gave birth to electronics and thus became a recent ancestor of modern automation. Before the turn of the century Marconi, Fessenden, De Forest and several other inventors and promoters had a clear-cut objective—to signal through space without wires. A supporting corps of teen-age amateurs avidly studied the new art and were poised to step into the shoes of the pioneers—sometimes, indeed, before the latter had quite stepped out of them. In retrospect the main development and its collateral branches—even the errors—can be seen moving along fairly straight and logical lines. In contrast, automation was middle-aged before anyone knew it had been born, and the genealogy swallows its own tail, for while latter-day automation is indeed the grandchild of radio and the child of electronics, the beginnings antedate the Industrial Revolution by several decades, and at least one astonishingly developed form was concurrent with it.

Labels like "Industrial Revolution" have their uses, but this revolution took a hundred years even if we arbitrarily start it at 1750 and terminate it at 1850—and that ignores the great voyages of discovery of the fifteenth and sixteenth centuries (including the discovery of America), the rise of capitalism in the seventeenth century, and much progress in mining, manufacturing, and the utilization of water power. Some accounts make it seem that the whole movement hinged on the "invention" of the steam engine by James Watt. Watt was a great innovator, but he didn't start from scratch; nobody does in technology. There was a commercially successful steam engine long before Watt was born, invented by an ironmonger or blacksmith named Thomas Newcomen. Some Newcomen engines remained in use until 1830. And Newcomen had predecessors too.

The first clearly discernible steps toward automation were taken in connection with the Newcomen and Watt engines. In the early 1700's the copper, tin, and coal mines of Britain were being flooded as the workings went deeper. The Newcomen engine met an urgent economic need: one owner took £10,000 out of a tin mine after one of Newcomen's contraptions cleared it of water. It consisted of a boiler, a large cylinder with an ill-fitting piston, and, surmounting the whole, a balance or working beam somewhat like those installed on paddle-wheel steamboats on American rivers a century and a half later. Steam was admitted to the cylinder and condensed by injection of

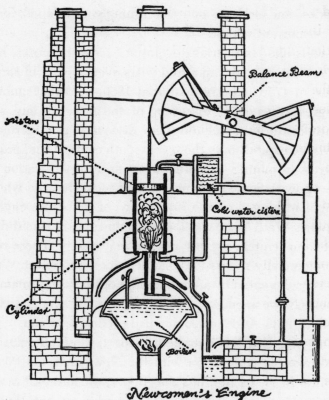

Newcomen's Engine

a stream of cold water; this created a partial vacuum under the piston, which was slammed to the other end of the cylinder by atmospheric pressure; the motion was transferred to the pump by the beam overhead; steam was then re-admitted and re-condensed—and the engine puffed through this sequence hour after hour.

Obviously the timing was critical. Both the steam and the condensing water were controlled by manually operated valves. Each valve had to be opened and closed at just the right point in the cycle. It was a setup for automation. There is some evidence that Newcomen himself devised an automatic control which regulated the speed of the engine to prevent exhaustion of the steam in the boiler, but the valves were usually operated by a boy, and according to Samuel Smiles, the Victorian moralizer and technological historian, it was a boy who made this invention. "To escape the drudgery and obtain an interval for rest, or perhaps for play, a boy named Humphrey Potter, who turned the cocks, set himself some method of evading his task. . . . Observing the alternate ascent and descent of the beam above his head, he bethought him of applying the movement to the alternate raising and lowering of the levers which governed the cocks. The result was the contrivance of what he called the *scoggan,* consisting of a catch worked by strings from the beam of the engine. [Smiles explains that *scoggan* comes from *scogging,* a North Country word meaning to skulk (shirk) one's work.] The action of the machine was thus made automatic; and the arrangement, though crude, not only enabled Potter to enjoy his play, but had the effect of improving the working power of the engine itself; the number of strokes which it made being increased from six or eight to fifteen or sixteen in the minute."

The invention, whether legendary or real, meets all the tests of automation—open-end in this instance. It eliminates robotlike labor by making the machine do for itself what was previously done by man—or boy. It does it better than the man could do it and so increases output and leisure for the worker. And, also in accordance with the formula, Potter was upgraded. He made the purported invention in 1713 and in 1720 we hear of him in Hungary, installing the first Newcomen engine there.

The basic limitations of the engine remained. The primary trouble was that the cylinder was cooled every time water was injected and had to be reheated some fifteen times a minute. In consequence the engine wasted 99 per cent of its fuel and was a notorious coal-hog; it was not unusual for the larger ones to consume thirteen tons daily. Watt, a mathematical-instrument maker at the University of Glasgow and a high-powered scientific analyst, saw that this defect was incurable without some radical departure. The solution came to him at the start of his usual Sunday walk around the Glasgow Green—to condense the steam in a separate vessel while keeping the cylinder hot at all times. Before he had completed the circuit of the Green the essential parts and operating functions of a much more efficient reciprocating engine were clear in his mind. He was twenty-nine years old at the time.

The engine Watt patented in 1769 did not depend on atmospheric pressure; the piston was moved by the pressure of the steam. Efficiency in terms of pounds of coal consumed per horsepower-hour was two or three times that of the Newcomen engine; Watt's first engine, that is, wasted only 97 per cent of the fuel, later models still less. Valve action was of course automatic; by that time others had improved on Potter's (or Newcomen's) strings. A further advance in automation technique came with Watt's invention of the flyball governor in 1788. Heretofore the speed of the engine had been controlled manually by a throttle valve. The governor made the engine regulate its own speed with greater precision and a saving of labor. The engine shaft drove the governor. As the speed increased, the balls were impelled outward by centrifugal force; this movement was utilized to decrease the supply of steam to the cylinder. When the engine slowed down, the balls would collapse inwards and the valve would open to admit more steam.

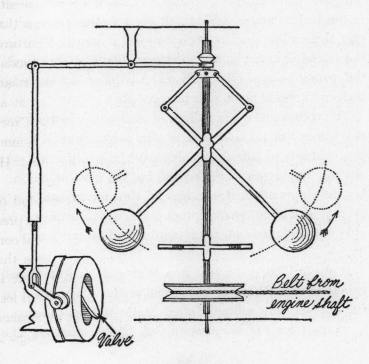

Valve

Belt from engine shaft

For the times, this was quite sophisticated automatic control. Feedback was involved through the use of a small part of the engine's output to regulate the steam input. Watt had closed the loop.

The steam engines built by Watt and his partner, the manufacturing genius Matthew Boulton, could run mills where water power was lacking and had the advantage of constancy instead of fluctuating with the seasons. At the same time the demands of the steam engine itself made for rapid progress in the mechanic arts, not only in Birmingham and Manchester but, with a lag of a few decades, in the United States, where two great figures emerged to play their roles upon the technological stage. Eli Whitney is a textbook name known to every schoolboy, though for the wrong reason. Oliver Evans is without honor in his own country and among his own people.

The cotton gin was no slight invention but neither was it Whitney's major achievement. His demonstration of the practicability of interchangeable parts in manufacture was not only the biggest thing he did, but the most revolutionary development in the Industrial Revolution and a key prerequisite of automated production, which is inconceivable without precision manufacture and interchangeability.

It was in 1789, just a year after Watt patented the flyball governor, that Whitney proposed to the government of the not yet very united United States the conclusion of a contract for the manufacture of 10,000 muskets. The

States had triumphed in the Revolution with the aid of France, but the French were now having a revolution of their own and, then as now, the allies of yesterday might be the enemies of tomorrow. Consequently guns were needed, and in quantity. Guns had always been made one at a time by a gunsmith. The gun was his as the child was its mother's, and in both cases production was slow. The gunsmith made all the parts and fitted them together. There would be a general similarity among the guns made in the same shop, but the parts of one gun would not fit another, even when the two guns had been made by the same gunsmith.

Whitney reasoned that it would be more efficient to have one man, or a group, make a particular part to a pattern, using power-driven machine tools as far as possible, and then to assemble the guns from these standardized stocks, locks, barrels, and so on. He was driven to this technique not only because he saw its inherent necessity in mass production but because of a shortage of skilled mechanics, which is one of the arguments for automation today. With the proposed technique Whitney expected to use mainly semiskilled or unskilled workers.

Whitney did not originate interchangeability but he made advances so significant that they overshadowed everything that had been done in printing, the manufacture of pins and nails, and other arts. Technological innovation calls for the right man at the right time. If he comes too late he is anticipated. If he comes too early he will wish he had never been born. For Whitney the time was ripe and he was the man. Someone else would have done it if he had not, but that someone else would have had to be a genius such as Whitney was.

Whitney worked out specialized devices for the job: jigs and patterns. A *jig* is a shape of wood or metal through or along which a tool moves to produce replicas. Thus a ruler is a jig for drawing a straight line; a metal sheet with holes in it is a jig for drilling holes in the configuration determined by the holes in the sheet. Holes can be drilled much faster with such a guide than if they were laid out on each separate piece. Whitney also built, and in some cases invented, special machine tools for the kind of mass production he had in mind. He took advantage of, and contributed to, the great advances in machine-tool design in England which were to continue over into the nineteenth century, and in the United States as well.

Whitney's guns were not quite so accurate as the best guns made by hand, but they were good guns which could be turned out fast and inexpensively. Whitney, whose cotton gin had been shamelessly pirated, made money in arms manufacture.

Oliver Evans was a contemporary of Watt's; the two died in the same year—1819—but Evans' life was not as long; he was born in 1755, Watt in 1736. Whitney was a farm boy who went to Yale, Evans a farm boy with only an elementary-school education. Compare his fame with his achievements:

1. In 1804 he built a steam-powered amphibious dredge for the City of Philadelphia and drove it through the

streets and into the Delaware River, where it outdistanced sailing craft.

2. He planned to build a steamboat but, with forbearance unusual in inventors, gave up the idea because he considered that John Fitch had preceded him.

3. He advocated the use of steam for railroads. In reduction to practice he was anticipated by his opposite number in England, Richard Trevithick, the Cornish strong man and wrestler, likewise an inventor of great daring and ingenuity.

4. He was for many years the leading builder of steam engines in the United States and made a better one than Watt and Boulton. Watt worked with a pressure of seven or eight pounds to the square inch, scarcely more than the pressure of a modern home steam-heating plant. When his young assistant Murdock wanted to proceed to higher pressures, Watt dissuaded him on the ground of the danger of explosion. The danger was real, but no one dissuaded Evans (or Trevithick either). Evans built engines at 100 pounds' pressure and with horsepowers up to 100. When he died, 50 of his engines were in commercial operation; one was designed for 200 pounds' pressure.

5. In 1795 Evans published a book on flour-milling which passed through fifteen editions and remained in print until the Civil War.

6. In 1785, without benefit of electricity, electronics, or any of the instrumentalities of modern engineering, this self-taught farm boy devised a completely automated flour mill which one man could operate—or which would

operate by itself—and which produced cleaner and more uniform flour than conventional mills.

To understand the magnitude of this achievement we must view it against the then current background of common-sense technique of production by disparate movements, using human or animal power, and mechanical power, when available, for the harder tasks. In a gristmill, for instance, the millstones would be turned by wind or water power, later by steam, but when grain was to be lifted to the upper level of the mill it would be carried upstairs in sacks or poured into a basket to be hoisted for a second man on top to empty. A mind like Evans' was as far beyond such clumsy stop-and-go, go-and-stop operation as the latter was beyond the techniques of prehistoric man. Evans thought through and mechanized the entire process from the delivery of the grain to the packaging of the flour. Why not hoist the grain in buckets on a continuous belt, or by a screw turning within a pipe, driven by the same power that turned the millstones? Or, when the meal was to be spread evenly, instead of employing a "hopper boy," why not resort to a revolving rake, similarly power-driven? Where other millers stomped through the grain, leaving dried mud from their boots to be mixed with the flour, why not arrange matters so that the product was never touched by human hands—or feet—during the whole sequence of operations?

It was no accident that the closest approach to full automation possible at this stage was first applied to flour-milling. Basically there are two methods of processing materials: batch and continuous-flow. The batch method was employed in the processing of bathtub gin in prohibition days and is still in use, albeit on a larger and more respectable scale, in many industrial operations. The modern tendency is, however, toward continuous-flow and processing while the material is in motion. Milling was an early continuous-flow industry.

Evans' brother, who traveled extensively in efforts, usually unsuccessful, to collect royalties on Oliver's inventions, often found flour mills locked but in operation, with not a soul in or near the premises. Having been provided with a supply of meal, the mill would run without attendance. Although there was no great eagerness to share the profits with the inventor, Evans' ideas encountered less resistance than those of many innovators both before and after him. George Washington was one of those who received a license under Evans' patents, used it in the construction of a flour mill at Mount Vernon, and besought Evans to find a miller who would work for the modest wages General Washington felt able to pay.

After Evans' death, progress in automation may be compressed into two time intervals of almost exactly equal length: 1820–1881 and 1882–1942. The point of separation is Edison's introduction of central-station electric power in 1881, and the point of termination is the beginning of World War II, where we turn from history to current developments dominated by the Big Three of mid-twentieth-century technology: electronics, atomic power, and automation.

In a history of this scope we cannot hope even to mention all the outstanding inventions and their interconnections, nor to trace their relationship to something which as yet had neither habitation nor name nor sponsors. Take a seemingly minor item like the electric relay, for instance. A relay is a remote-controlled, electrically operated switch. The earliest forms were on telegraph systems. Automatic switching in telephony, which is one of modern automation's pathbreaking forms, is done by means of complex arrangements of specialized relays, and, in fact, no modern technological system could be operated without dozens, even thousands of such devices, with power-handling capacity ranging from the very small to the very large. What is true of relays is equally true of measuring instruments. What industry calls "know-how" is really "know-how-much." In a progressive technological setup you can't just guess at electrical voltages and currents, the flow of liquids, the pressure of gases, the temperature of furnaces, and other physical quantities. Advanced instrumentation is not only vital to automation, but integral with it.

In the 1820–1881 interval we can only mention sewing machines, power looms, typewriters and other business machines, mass-produced clocks and watches, agricultural machinery, composing machines in printing, machines for shoemaking and steelmaking and meat-packing, and automatic air-braking, among other machines and devices which marked advances in mechanization, communication, and control. And of course, toward the end of the period, there is the invention of the telephone: without Alexander Graham Bell and the Bell Telephone Laboratories, we would lack both the techniques and the technological climate in which systems like automation flourish. On the political side, at the two-thirds mark of the period, there is the Civil War which, as all modern wars do, promoted mechanization, monopoly, and social change. And which taught that, other things being equal and sometimes when they are unequal, victory is to the strong in machines.

By making electricity abundant, Edison made possible a multitude of inventions which in turn made modern mass production and automation possible. Edison, of course, was not alone in electrical development, and in one of the pigheaded fits which were intermingled with his genius he actually obstructed the transition from direct to alternating current for long-distance transmission. This was largely the creation of European engineers and the Westinghouse and General Electric teams, including such redoubtable theoreticians and inventors as Charles P. Steinmetz and Nikola Tesla. The great pioneer of electric traction and application of electric motors to production, Frank Julian Sprague, is also among those to whom we owe modern electric power. Still, Edison is first among his peers. It was Edison, also, who institutionalized invention; his laboratory at West Orange, New Jersey, was the precursor of the great research organizations of today.

Any great innovation works both forwards and backwards in time and thus turns earlier failures into successes. Thomas Davenport of Vermont (a blacksmith, like Thomas Newcomen), utilizing the epoch-making discoveries of Joseph Henry, invented an electric motor in 1837. Davenport's motors operated tools in his small shop, but batteries were the only source of electricity then available. The electric generating and distribution system had to come to maturity before the electric motor could power the production line.

Much productive thinking also had to be done before the production line could become a reality. In any engineering project reason must play a part, otherwise it wouldn't work at all. But the amount of reason which will make it work, after a fashion, may be quite small. With all his engineering genius and originality, Eli Whitney could not think of a better method of manufacturing his interchangeable parts than to shuffle them around the factory for the various operations required. This practice was to continue for another hundred years and the proportion of rule-of-thumb, tradition, and sheer craft superstition remained large in industry. But in the late eighties a scientifically minded foreman in a steel plant, Frederick Winslow Taylor, began the practice of "efficiency engineering"—stressing the time-and-motion studies, systematic cost accounting, standardization of labor, regularity, continuity, synchronization, and relentless hunting-down of waste which underlie flow or line production, with the workpieces moving in a continuous line and the machines located sequentially along the line,—which was to culminate in Henry Ford's power-driven moving-chassis assembly line and eventually in the automated production line.

The Ford assembly line was first installed at the Highland Park plant in Detroit in January, 1914. Oliver Evans, in working out his early brand of automation, had supplied many of the basic ideas which later technicians utilized, usually without knowing whence they came, but Evans had the relatively simple task of applying successive processing steps to a single undifferentiated product, while Ford's problem was to assemble numerous parts and subassemblies into a highly complicated machine. By the tireless ingenuity with which he and his co-workers combined pre-existing elements into a main assembly line fed by subsidiary lines, all tightly synchronized and coordinated, they succeeded in evolving something new: an automobile which almost any American could own or hope to own and which could be mass-produced with steadily increasing output and (for a while) steadily decreasing price.

On this assembly line—which produced 15 million cars up to the time the Model T, then costing about $300, was discontinued in 1927—a kind of automation was in use, but since the machines and control techniques of what we understand by automation were not yet available, men were used as machines. The same thing was being done elsewhere, if on a smaller scale, and tentative efforts were being made to replace the automatons of flesh and blood with the automatons of metal. The first transfer machine was installed at the Morris Motors plant at Coventry, England, in 1924. It consisted of a series of automatic-cycle machines lined up with means for automatically shuttling work from one machine to the next, and means, likewise automatic, for initiating the cycle of the following machine when work left the machine ahead of it in the line. The array produced cylinder blocks from rough castings. It worked, but it was ahead of its time; failing to save money, it was broken up into separate units. So Detroit automation apparently did not originate in Detroit, and had been tried—and failed commercially—even before the passing of the Model T.

In the same year that the Highland Park assembly line went into action, the first World War broke out. Notable progress was made in the art of mass slaughter, which likewise was being progressively mechanized to such good effect that some 15 per cent of those mobilized perished. In other branches of technology the greatest advances were in aircraft and electronics. Lee De Forest had invented the modern vacuum tube in 1907. For several years it was a fragile handmade product which often burned out in the first hour of use. But it had immense potentialities as an amplifier, whether of radio frequencies coming through space or the speech frequencies of telephone lines. Soon De Forest and Edwin Howard Armstrong, independently and to the accompaniment of acrimonious patent litigation which lasted nineteen years, developed a form of radio-frequency feedback which made the tube a generator of oscillations and spelled the end of spark gaps, arcs, alternators, and all other varieties of transmitters, and made radio telephony feasible. Three years after the end of the war, radio launched its first large-scale invasion of the entertainment industry: the broadcasting of speech and music. In another few years the phonograph was electronized and the silent movies were engulfed by radio-created techniques of sound recording and reproduction. The final step was taken after World War II, although it had been ready before: the broadcasting of both sound and picture in television.

With these growing markets and resources, electronics spawned measuring and control devices related to those used in reproduction of pictures and sound, devices so versatile and flexible that it is no exaggeration to say that in most fields of technology today every engineer must either be an electronics engineer or hire one. This applies especially to automation engineering, much of which, without electronics, would have only limited applicability.

Between the two World Wars the public demanded the comforts and conveniences of automatic control without much interest, as yet, in the art of automatic control as such, much less in its principles. Refrigerators, washing machines, and automatic heating were among the products which found a large market during the interwar period and brought automation unobtrusively into the home.

The same thing came to pass in other fields and in ways apparently unrelated. If you received a check or bill from a technologically progressive organization, or merely a big one, it was likely to be pierced with a multiplicity of slits which were obviously a code for automatic handling in business machines. If you were a military reservist called to active duty, what you were to the personnel boards, actually, was a large card with punched holes corresponding to your particular qualifications. The holes were electrically sensed by a machine, your card fell into a basket, was inspected and passed on to a typist who cut a stencil and sent you to war.

Business cards go back to Joseph Marie Jacquard, the French inventor who used punched steel cards in the late eighteenth century to program his automatic loom, but the mechanization of business really began with the invention of a calculating machine by the mathematician and philosopher Blaise Pascal in 1642. Pascal was a prodigy in

many fields and this was one of his minor creations, tossed off when he was nineteen to help his father check his accounts. Another versatile genius, Gottfried Wilhelm von Leibnitz, the inventor of the differential calculus, took some interest in the theory of communication and computing machines later in the seventeenth century, but nothing much was done until Charles Babbage, a British accountant, produced a commercial adding machine in 1873 and planned, but did not succeed in building, an "analytical engine" which is the prototype of the general-purpose digital computers of today. The Babbage "engine" was to have been equipped with an internal memory, an arithmetic unit capable of performing addition, subtraction, multiplication and division, and means for carrying out long sequences of instructions. For feeding data into and out of the machine and giving the machine its instructions, Babbage planned to use Jacquard's punched cards—another instance of cross-fertilization in invention.

Once men turned to machines to amplify their powers and ease their labor, all these developments were inevitable. The growth of machines is like that of children. When they are young, everything must be done for them, even the simplest things like the manual operation of the valves in the Newcomen engine. As they mature, they are able to do more and more for themselves and finally to regulate themselves with only occasional human intervention: then we have automation. We can see that, even at this point in history, before World War II and before the word had been coined, automation was an organic development of technology, gradually coming into being as technology became so complex that automatic control was not only desirable but essential to perform the tasks that society imposes.

CHAPTER 4

The Machines

IF THIS were a big book rather than a small one, and all of it, rather than a single section, devoted to the applications of automation, it still would not suffice for anything like a complete account. Even a hurried survey is not useless, however. A few years hence things will look quite different, but the trends and principles will be much the same, for, as we have seen, automation is actually a more mature art than first impressions would indicate.

Communication

Communication from men to machines we call *control*. Control also involves communication from machines to men, which is growing at a prodigious rate: we shall see why in a moment. Another booming field is communication among machines: Frederick R. Kappel, president of the American Telephone and Telegraph Company, in a speech

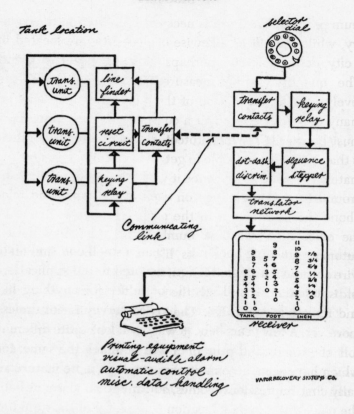

Tank location

selector dial

trans. unit

trans. unit

trans. unit

line finder

reset circuit

transfer contacts

keying relay

Communicating link

transfer contacts

keying relay

dot-dash discrim.

sequence stepper

translator network

receiver

TANK   FOOT   INCH

Printing equipment
visual-audible alarm
automatic control
misc. data handling

VAPOR RECOVERY SYSTEMS CO.

before the Economics Club of Chicago, said, "Already we see the need for transmitting tremendous amounts of raw data. We expect that as time goes on the amount of communication between machines in different cities may be as large as the amount of communication between people."

Telemetering—measuring at a distance—has grown apace with automation. Suppose an oil company has a tank farm, an area studded with tanks containing some petroleum product. The farm is necessarily located in the country, while the offices, likewise of necessity, are located in a city, perhaps nearby, perhaps hundreds of miles distant. The quantity to be measured is a simple one—the level of the liquid in each of the tanks. But there may be many tanks dispersed over a considerable area, since they must be spaced for fire protection. Another consideration is that it may be desirable to get all the readings at approximately the same time; hence it won't do just to send a man around to read the gauge on each of the tanks and telephone the information to the office. Instead, someone in the office dials the tank number and the tank queried automatically telegraphs its liquid level over the same wire or radio circuit to the receiver, where the tank number is displayed together with the liquid level in feet, inches, and fractions of an inch. The system can be made much more elaborate than this: it will print the readings on a roll of paper by means of a "slave" electric typewriter which is actuated by electromagnetic plungers mechanically connected with the keys, and sound an alarm at both the office and the tank location if the level of the liquid in any of the tanks should approach the overflow point.

There is no limit except economic expediency to telemetering, either in distance or data to be transmitted. By means of *transducers*, which convert mechanical information such as pressures into electrical information, and electrical *tachometers*, which do the same thing for revolving machinery, and a host of other telemetering devices, measurements along a natural-gas pipeline, for instance, can be printed on the teletypewriters at a central point hundreds or thousands of miles away.

Another variety of communication between machine and man goes under the name of *airborne data acquisition*. When the airborne vehicle is a missile, air-to-ground tele-metering is the usual recourse, since records made in flight are likely to be destroyed when the missile returns to earth. In testing manned aircraft the collection of a large amount of data by recording in flight is necessary for future design; it is also necessary because rapid communi-cation between aircraft and pilot may be a matter of life and death for both. The pilot can no longer fly by his wits, experience, intuition, such instruments as he can manage to read in a few seconds, and the seat of his pants. Aircraft have become so fast, complex, and highly stressed that all these techniques may leave the aircraft with only one means of talking back to the pilot: disintegration in the air.

Automation, however, can solve this problem, like many others. The aircraft may be equipped with strain gauges at critical structural points. The values measured by these gauges are constantly and automatically compared with a standard which represents the safe loading of the struc-ture at that point. If the safe value is equaled or exceeded, an electronic tube in the system "fires," actuating a relay which connects power to a warning light. In addition to the warning, the system may be designed to take action to relieve the strain by rectifying or superseding the pilot's control of the aircraft.

Safety and the continued growth of the aviation industry

devolve on the intensive application of automation to air travel. The Air Transport Association estimated in 1955 that four near-collisions occurred daily in the United States under the conditions then prevailing and which were— and are—getting worse all the time. Various types of automatic proximity-warning devices are being developed to avert catastrophes like the collision of two airliners over the Grand Canyon in 1956, with the loss of 128 lives. But with new commercial planes under development which will be capable of closing on each other at 1500 miles an hour—25 miles a minute, almost ½ mile a second—these are only stopgaps. The ultimate answer—and it had better not be too ultimate—is a fully automatic system of ground control in which computers, constantly fed with information on all flights in an area, will calculate flight paths and traffic patterns and in effect control all the planes in the air within range of a ground station.

Going Places

Communication is movement of information; transportation is movement of physical objects, animate or inanimate. There is no sharp dividing line between the two. Our experience of anything is only the sum of the information we get through our senses. And that includes people. If one could transmit *all* the information about a human being and reassemble it in the original relationship at the other end, the result would be indistinguishable from the original. Norbert Wiener discusses the possibility of thus telegraphing a man (*The Human Use of Human Beings*) but he points out the difficulty of scanning the man's tissues without destroying them. However remote, it is an intriguing prospect, particularly in relation to movie actresses and other nice girls who, as things stand, don't get around nearly enough.

The more mundane applications of automation in transportation, like most of automation, have developed gradually from modest beginnings. Since about 1925 the London Post Office has been operating an underground parcel railway with small crewless trains. Since about the same time the New York subway system has been automated to the extent that a train can't start if somebody has one foot or hand in the door. Here we see the mystique of feedback at its best. Since there is always some New Yorker prepared to hold up a thousand other New Yorkers as long as he can board a train which is ready to pull out of the station, the railroad has to hire men to override the feedback and close the doors by force during the rush hours.

On longer if less congested railroads, automation has taken over much of the dispatching, with impressive savings in trackage, maintenance, and taxes. Trains can operate in either direction on a single track equipped with sidings at higher speeds than on two one-way tracks previously. With two two-way tracks, fast freights can be run past slow freights, and passenger trains past the fast freights. Another saving is in the "push-button" freight yards which are becoming commonplace all over the country. In a big freight yard there may be fifty or sixty miles of track and a couple of thousand cars a day to be assembled into new trains before going on their way. Each car, or a group with the same destination, is pulled onto a "hump" from which it rolls to the appropriate track. Using electronic equipment, a yardmaster in a control tower, working from prearranged lists, directs the cars to the correct tracks. As a car moves, a computerlike device evaluates the factors that affect its rollability—weight, wind, and so on—and regulates a retarder brake in the track under the car so that it moves gently to the car to which it is to be coupled.

Automation is also being applied—but not fast enough—to the problems of urban automobile and pedestrian traffic. The fixed type of traffic light is too unadaptable: there may be no traffic on green and a dozen cars waiting on red, but the light has no way of sensing this or doing anything about it. "Traffic-responsive" signals are beginning to supplant these maladjusted robots. A pressure pad in the pavement, or an overhead radar unit, counts avenue and cross-street traffic and a computer adjusts the period of the light for maximum flow of traffic. Pedestrians can get a green light by pushing a button.

Application of automatic control to automobiles directly still has a long way to go. The first use in the United States of automatic transmissions to free the driver of manual gear-shifting was on a few GMC buses in 1934. The object was to enable the driver to make change with his right hand while the bus was in motion, steer with his left hand, yell at the passengers to move to the rear, glare at taxi drivers, and answer the passengers' questions, all at the same time. From buses the automatic transmission spread to private cars. There is some talk now of automatic devices for steering a car into a parking space, preventing it from skidding, and even steering and stopping it on the road. Chrysler has a picture of a "Highway Cruiser" tearing along a parkway at 100 miles an hour with a happy family—mother, father, and two children—sitting around inside as if they were in their living room. The car is being steered by radar beams. But don't look for anything like this on next year's models, or those of the year after next.

Automation is, however, making heavy inroads in vertical transportation. The Otis Elevator Company has developed a system in which a special-purpose computer continually analyzes traffic demand and supplants not only the operators but the starter. The computer is assisted by an automatic weighing device which runs a car express when it is filled and bypasses all floors except those called by passengers. When people get out, the car again makes stops to take on passengers. "Entirely electronic and completely automatic, this device is consistent in operation and is free from errors caused by fatigue in human attendants," the Otis people point out. And also saves their salaries. For its part, the Westinghouse Electric Corporation, through its renowned elevator expert, Betty Furness, claims savings of $7,000 a year per car, and the Westinghouse electronic door control, says Betty, will outperform even highly trained human operators. And when the car is improperly operated or the passengers obstruct traffic, either the automatic elevators will tell them where to get off by means of a tape-recorded repertory of messages, or gently give them the bum's rush by nudging them out of the way.

Toward the Automatic Factory

The familiar photographs of 300-foot-long transfer machines portray such a labyrinth of motors, wiring, and unintelligible metal parts, that despite the obvious order, symmetry, and repetition, one wonders how either engine blocks or human beings can find their way from one end to the other. But things aren't as bad as they look. When the photographers come in, the operators are shooed out of the setup, so that the picture will show only one man—for once, not a model in décolletage and a prop smile—looking lost and lonely amid this phantasmagoria of mechanism. Actually, quite a few people are kept around to maintain the flow of 4,500 engine blocks a day through the maze, and when the photographers leave, these technicians return. But despite their presence, one of these highly automated production lines is a marvel of technological achievement and surely as much a wonder of the world as the seven of the ancients.

The over-all economic importance of these splendid mechanical monsters may be less, however, for the present, than that of smaller automatic or semiautomatic machine tools which are on the job in far greater numbers and whose photographs appear only in the trade papers. Formerly, at each conventional lathe, drill press, milling machine, or other machine tool there stood a vigilant (and skilled) operator, who during a good part of the time was doing something or other in active collaboration with the machine. Shaping the part in accordance with a blueprint, he would make a cut, measure or gauge the part, make another cut, consult the blueprint, and so on. Even with the advent of templates and guides the frequent attention of the operator was still required. These standard machines were versatile but slow; because they were slow, and required skilled attendance, they were expensive to operate.

Special machine tools came in with mass production, especially of automobiles, and were designed to turn out the same part over and over. But the operator still had to watch and push buttons at the right instant to keep the sequence going. Further automation has made it unnecessary to do more than start the sequence, after which the machine will run through it until the part is completed. "Lathe," a trade-paper advertisement reads, "can run approximately an 8-hour shift without attention, except for an occasional check by operator to make sure parts are being delivered to the loading mechanism." Numerous relays and other complex electrical devices contribute to this type of automation. A dynamic braking system, for instance, brings the motor to a quick stop when the sequence is complete, so that the part can be unloaded without loss of production time.

Mechanization leads to more mechanization, automation

to more automation. A gigantic press at a Kaiser Metal Products plant stamps out bathtubs. Formerly two men removed the stampings between strokes. Now an "iron hand" darts in as soon as the tub has been stamped, raises it, and swings it to a conveyor. The saving of the men's wages isn't as important as the speeding up of the press which the absence of human hands makes possible. Other models of unloading and feeding machines can handle anything from small stampings to automobile roofs.

Most automation in manufacture is introduced piece-meal, with one innovation necessitating another. But this isn't high style in the automation world. The leaders prefer integrated to improvised automation, not only on techno-logical-esthetic grounds, but on the grounds that this approach will justify itself economically. Their ultimate aim is nothing less than a whole factory run by a computer. But how can a computer run a factory? Let us see, first, how it can run a single complex machine.

Actually there is nothing mysterious in the relationship

between the computer or data-processing machine and a metalworking machine. It is a matter of furnishing information to the latter—*command information,* the automation engineers call it. Since the metalworking machine furnishes its own power, all that it needs to fashion a part is numerical data on where and what to cut. Except that we are communicating the information to a machine instead of a man, there is nothing very novel about this. If you say to a lathe operator, "Turn a shaft 1 inch in diameter and 18 inches long," all you are giving him is numerical data, and all he does is to translate these data into movements of the lathe. Actually, even in a small shop, it isn't that simple: a formidable amount of verbal and written data-transfer is involved. To turn out a single metal part requires a design sketch, then blueprints showing several views, then a methods-planning sheet, then operations-breakdown sheets and detailed breakdown sheets for each machinist. It is because oral and paper communication between men and men and between men and machines is so slow, complex, ambiguous, and expensive that it pays to bring in data-processing machines.

When machine communicates with machine, the instructions are necessarily in physical form, such as pulses or bursts of electricity—"command pulses"—or other signals. The Giddings & Lewis Machine Tool Company has developed one such system in cooperation with the General Electric Company and the Massachusetts Institute of Technology. It is in commercial use for controlling skin mills for milling wing panels of aircraft, and other machine tools.

The Machines

The control starts in an engineering office, with numerical data on size and shape which may be obtained from working drawings of the part to be made, and information on machining of the metal to be used. All this information, in ordinary decimal form, is recorded on paper tapes in a tape-punching business machine. A simple machine might be operated with paper tape directly, or with punched business cards. In the airplane-wing case, however, the directions are too complicated for this method, and the paper tapes are run through a computer-type machine which translates the decimal data into equivalent electrical modulation or variations. These signals from a number of paper tapes are recorded on a single magnetic tape in a recorder much like a tape recorder for music, but this recorder has 14 channels and can record as many as 14 tracks on the magnetic tape. The tape then contains, in electrically reproducible, sequential form, all the information originally fed into the system in decimal form.

The scene now shifts to the factory. Near the machine to be directed there is a playback which will reproduce the electrical signals which were originally fed into the magnetic tape recorder. These signals from the 14 tracks, or as many of them as are needed, are fed into a bank of amplifiers and power-controllers which guide the movements and cutting action of the cutting tools.

This description gives only a faint idea of what is involved; for one thing, it neglects feedback, which corrects any deviations by a complicated process of automatic comparison. But, complicated as the method is, savings are

Office

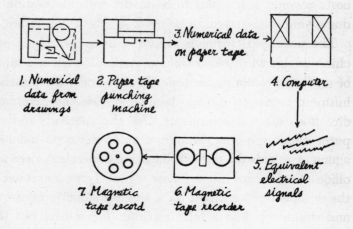

1. Numerical data from drawings
2. Paper tape punching machine
3. Numerical data on paper tape
4. Computer
5. Equivalent electrical signals
6. Magnetic tape recorder
7. Magnetic tape record

Factory

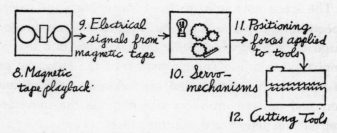

8. Magnetic tape playback.
9. Electrical signals from magnetic tape
10. Servo-mechanisms
11. Positioning forces applied to tools
12. Cutting Tools

reported to run so high that the general adoption of tape control seems to be assured in small as well as large machine shops. Manufacturers unable to invest in their own computers and tape-recording equipment can take their blueprints to a computing center, as housewives take their wash to a washing- and drying-machine center—but it costs considerably more than 65 cents to hire tape-producing equipment!

The next step is a comprehensive data-processing machine which will give electrical instructions to a battery of machines and also take over clerical duties, correlating information on output, marketing conditions, inventory, etc., and making decisions of a routine nature. The computer, then, will take over some of the functions of management as well as those of rank-and-file employees in the office and factory. This should surprise no one. Some of the decisions of management, however disguised by pomp and ritual, are of a mechanical nature. Robert A. Lovett, the investment banker and former Secretary of Defense, has said that most of the decisions of commercial banking could be made by a computer. But by far the most promising combination is creative management *and* a computer.

The automatized engine production line may be the most spectacular contemporary example of automation on a large scale, but it is not the most important. Automobile engines can be made in conventional factories and most of them are. Where advanced automation is vital is in the continuous-process industries, in particular the petroleum, petro-chemical, chemical, and atomic-energy industries. An oil refinery is an outdoor factory which may be twenty-five stories high and cover acres of ground. The operation must be centralized if only because manual control at local points would entail so many communication difficulties, misunderstandings, and delays that the plant would be in a chronic state of near or actual breakdown. Even with the best instrumentation and the most skilled human supervision such a plant does get into difficulty once in a while. At these times instrumentation and recording are equally essential to get it back to normal and for autopsic purposes. Hence there are many recording instruments which tell not only of present conditions but of what happened a minute, an hour, or twenty-four hours ago.

The instruments are grouped in a control room, three walls of which may be entirely covered with instrument and control panels. These panels are essentially a flow diagram of the plant, and modern practice is to use distinctive colors to represent the various water, steam, air, catalyst, and crude-oil pipes and the products into which the crude oil is converted, such as gasolines, fuel oils, and lubricants. Instruments are located along these lines to show temperature, pressure, rate of flow, viscosity, etc., of raw, partly processed, and finished materials; storage-tank levels; and other variables. Off-normal values actuate alarm systems which alert the operators by audio-visual means—lights, horns, sirens. Some parts of the system may be self-stabilizing: deviations from the norm automatically result in corrective measures. The impression that these plants are completely automated is, however, mistaken. They are highly instrumented, but most of the decisions are made by the operators, who must be part chemist, part physicist, part engineer, and part clairvoyant. Experts believe that automation at the computer level will not replace men as the decision-makers in such plants, but will enable them to make better decisions on the basis of better information. And with better information, output can be improved, both quantitatively and qualitatively, to a very substantial—and profitable—degree.

The Automation of War

Military automation is not a matter of economics, but, like automation for civil aircraft, a matter of necessity. A manufacturer of fire-control systems says of one of them that it is designed "to perform a task beyond the scope of human capabilities." The pilot cannot find his target without airborne radar. He cannot aim his guns, taking into account in fractions of a second the motion of his own aircraft, the motion of the target, projectile characteristics, and half a dozen other factors, so a special-purpose computer must be provided to enable him to bring the enemy down. The enemy, of course, is automated too: it is a battle of men and computers. The victor cannot get back to base without more automation in the form of navigational aids.

Over human adversaries the fighter pilot and the bomber crews may be victorious, but they are being automated out of existence. What the yeoman's longbow and gunpowder did for the mounted knight in armor, the surface-to-air missile is doing for the fighter pilot. On a larger scale, the Russians are developing intercontinental missiles to come over here, while we are developing missiles to go

over there, and again automation is the decisive factor.
The career officers of the Army, Navy, and Air Force are
in the position of businessmen whose industries are threat-
ened with extinction by technological progress. All are
frantically jumping aboard the technological bandwagon.
The Air Force is jumping fastest and farthest.

Existing intercontinental missiles which are more or
less operational are by the same token already obsolete.
The *Snark,* for instance, powered by a conventional air-
breathing jet engine and reaching a maximum altitude
of about 60,000 feet (manned airplanes have exceeded
90,000 feet) and flying at subsonic speeds, is merely a jet
airplane without a pilot. The ballistic missiles, the true
intercontinental types, are independent of the earth's
atmosphere. Their speed will be 20–25 times the speed of
sound, or about 12,000 mph. At the highest point of the
elliptical path the missile will be between 500 and 800
miles above the earth. It will be able to fly from New York
to Moscow in about 30 minutes. If it is ever fired in anger,
whether it will actually hit Moscow (or New York) is
arguable, but the designers hope it will be accurate to
within five or ten miles at a 5,000-mile range. Since it will
be carrying a thermonuclear warhead, it needn't be accurate.

The ICBM will be powered by rocket engines in the tail.
As each rocket engine expends its fuel, the controls will
drop it off and the lightened missile will fly faster. All the
fuel will be burned in the first three or four minutes of
flight. During this part of the path, a few hundred miles

long, the missile, weighing initially about 100 tons, is still under human control. It is followed by radar and sends back signals. Computers plot its trajectory and check its adjustments. If necessary, fuel can be shut off from the ground by radio or the missile can be put back on its predetermined path by tilting the motors or altering a rudder arrangement in the jet blast. After burn-out the missile is in free flight, like a shell, and mistakes or inaccurracies can no longer be corrected. Ultimately it is planned to equip missiles with means for *inertial navigation:* they will carry their own computers, gyroscopes, stabilizing devices and everything needed to keep them on target, require no contact with the earth or any other planet, and radiate no signals which an enemy might utilize.

The companies engaged in missile development advertise that theirs is "creative engineering of the highest order." There is actually a constructive aspect: the missiles, if they don't destroy mankind, will develop into space ships and, probably before the end of the century, carry men to the moon. The exploratory earth satellites to be launched during the 1957–1958 International Geophysical Year will be carried aloft by three-stage rockets.[*]

For the present, however, all other existing or possible aspects of space travel are subordinated to the military. At the same time, technology has destroyed the measure of

[*] The reader may learn all about space flight in another volume of Norton Primers for Our Times (Patrick Moore and Irving Geis: *Earth Satellites*).

security that superiority in arms once afforded. Until recently a war, for all its inhumanity and stupidity, could actually settle something, for a few years or even a few decades. True, in the long run all it led to was another war with a different configuration of allies, but in 1945, for instance, Hitler, Mussolini, and some other eminent Yahoos were certainly dead and the Axis powers were prostrate. But now small wars have become inconclusive and big wars mutually ruinous. The two military-technological superstates, accoutered with the superweapons neither dares to use, face each other on a world grown too small for modern battle.

Brains, Big and Little

We have referred to computers without describing the inward workings of these $1–6 million big "brains" or their little brothers at about $50,000. This "brain" stuff is misleading to begin with. Of course the electronic computer or calculating machine can perform routine mental operations so fast that the human brain isn't even in the running. No job is too tough for a well-designed and well-operated computing machine, provided it can be reduced to a sequence of equations or formulae or some other mechanical-logical basis. It is correct, therefore, to speak of "brain functions" in relation to a machine, and that term is sometimes used by the scientists who build and operate the electronic prodigies. But you never hear a programmer call a computer a brain, and if one came home from a hard day with an IBM 705 and his wife asked him, "Well, how was the giant brain today?" he'd be apt to give her a dirty look, if not a poke in the eye. The professional has even less use for "mechanical Einsteins" and other synthetic creations of hard-pressed science writers.

The fact is that computers, even the fastest and biggest of them and the still bigger, faster and more versatile ones coming up, not only can't emulate the essential qualities of an Einstein, a Keats, or a Bach; but a bus driver relaxing with his friends in a bar, or a high-school boy taking serious notice of a girl for the first time, or a chimpanzee, or a dog, even, has ideas, not to speak of emotions,

which are not within the competence of a machine, even if it can multiply a pair of 127-digit numbers and arrive at a 254-digit answer in $\frac{1}{3}$ second, or $\frac{1}{30}$ second. Nor does the ability of a computer to perform logical operations at fantastic speeds blur the distinction. Logic is not the same as thinking, much less wisdom. Logic is merely a technique for progressing from premises which may be false, to conclusions which, even though true, may be incomplete, or irrelevant, or misleading. Paranoiacs are often very logical, and if paranoid data were fed into a computer it would come up with paranoid answers.

The difference between a human and an electronic brain is quantitative as well as qualitative. A British scientist,

Lord Halsbury, has figured that the biggest computers constructed so far have only $\frac{1}{10,000}$ of the associative capacity of a common human brain. The IBM 702 weighs 28 tons. How is a mass of nerve tissue weighing three pounds capable of so much more than the massive machine? One reason is that the component parts of the brain are very small compared with vacuum tubes and transistors. A great deal of contemporary engineering activity is applied to "miniaturization"—making the organs of an earth satellite, for instance, as small as possible. But the molecules and polymer chains and cells making up the organs of living creatures are already miniaturized far beyond the power of man, and so there is room in the brain for an astronomical number—10 or 15 billion—of nerve cells and a vastly greater number of possible interconnections.

There is no question that computers will be greatly reduced in size and that for a given size the interconnectional capacity will be proportionately increased. Still the resemblance between computers constructed with smaller and smaller units, and brains, will remain superficial, simply because the brain operates as part of a self-conscious, feeling, willful creature with a unique life-experience. To build a brain one would have to build a man.

At the same time, precisely because the computer is a crude and predictable instrument, it may shed light on the design and functioning of its more complex and subtle counterpart. It is even possible that the new concepts of communication, information, and memory which are emerging from computer technology may ultimately bridge the gap between conscious knowledge and the immensely intricate physiological knowledge which enables the organs of the body to function individually and in concert, or which teaches a wasp to sting a caterpillar with the precise technique required to paralyze but not kill it, so that it will be preserved to feed the larvae of the wasp after the wasp itself is dead.

A general-purpose digital computer comprises the following units:

1. Input and output units through which the machine communicates with the world of men, receiving information to be processed and returning it in intelligible form (*read-out*). Since the machine is electronic, information must be presented to it in electronic or electronic-convertible form.

2. A control or programming unit which sets up instructions for the machine, including built-in or self-sequencing routines. Since the machine has no will of its own, it must be told electronically what to do, how to do it, and when to do it. The instructions may involve routines and subroutines wired into the machine and on tap for use whenever needed.

3. A memory unit in which both instructions and data are stored. The data in the memory unit are essentially reference information which the machine requires in order to deal with the problems presented to it. A location of data within the machine is called an *address*.

4. An arithmetic unit to add, subtract, multiply, and

divide. A machine which can add can do anything mathematical. Subtraction is only negative addition; it makes no difference to the machine whether it adds 70 and 60 pulses to make 130, or whether, having recorded 130, it brings it back to 70 by wiping out 60. If the machine has no special circuits for multiplication and division it can obtain the answers by multiple addition and subtraction. And, odd as it may seem, if one can compute fast enough it is feasible to solve complex mathematical functions by simple arithmetic, without resorting to the special techniques of higher mathematics.

Depending on what it has to do, a computer may have a big memory unit and a small arithmetic unit, or vice versa. In other words, there are highbrow computers which solve intricate scientific and technical problems and which must be very resourceful on the calculating end, and lowbrow computers which are mainly filing systems. An example of a computer which doesn't compute is an airplane seat-reservation machine, which is little more than a memory and communication system. It needs to subtract only up to the number of seats in an airplane—70 or so.

The input unit of a computer may operate from a manual keyboard, essentially an electric typewriter in reverse. When a key is depressed, the corresponding electric impulses are fed into the computer. Or punched business cards may be used, or punch marks in paper tape. Magnetic tape is another source of input signals. The output may be tape or card-punches, or an electric typewriter or other printer. Either input or output, or both, may be sent over wire or radio circuits.

Within the machine, digital information, including instructions in numerical code, is handled by mechanical, electromechanical, or electronic counting devices. Early computers used mechanical counters. A system of gears can count on its teeth as a child counts on its fingers. One gear can count units, the next tens, the one after that hundreds, and so on. Replacement of mechanical with electromechanical means began in the 1920's and computers with electromagnetically rotated gears or wheel-type counters were developed during World War II. Machines using telephone relays were also designed and are still in use. The dial telephone system is a gigantic system of this kind.

Because of the inertia of its parts, a relay takes a two-hundredth of a second or longer to respond. Electronic computers respond in a millionth of a second. The first electronic computer, ENIAC (*E*lectronic *N*umerical *I*ntegrator *A*nd *C*alculator), was put in operation in 1946. It was built for the Ballistic Research Laboratory at Aberdeen, Maryland by the Moore School of Electrical Engineering of the University of Pennsylvania. Although ENIAC is a kind of *Great Eastern* of computers—it has 18,000 vacuum tubes, weighs 30 tons, occupies 1500 square feet of floor space, and requires 150 kilowatts of power for operation—it was the answer to an ordnance man's prayer. It used to take 20 hours to work out values for a 60-second shell trajectory with a desk computer. ENIAC did it in 30 seconds—half the time the shell took to reach its target.

ENIAC uses decimal arithmetic. Modern machines have been considerably simplified through the use of binary arithmetic; the number of tubes in the current Remington-Rand, International Business Machines, and other large machines is only about 2500. While there are always problems of "debugging" and maintenance, these machines are kept in production at least 80 per cent of the time. They are operated around the clock and employ a whole staff of programmers and electronic valets. A large machine may cost a million dollars a year to operate. Naturally, big computers are only for big business, big science, and big government.

These machines employ a number of types of data-storage, or memory, none of which is entirely satisfactory: much high-powered and promising research is under way. The most widely used storage methods at the present time are magnetic. Small doughnut-shaped cores built up of magnetic alloy containing nickel, iron, and molybdenum in layers about $1/10,000$ inch thick (about a sixteenth of the thickness of a human hair) are wound with fine copper wire. These cores are magnetized by a current sent through the windings. Extensively used, also, are magnetic disks, drums, and tapes. The research pressure is in the direction of greater compactness and ease of access. RCA has a magnetic system under development which may accommodate over a million bits in a space the size of a shoebox.

Whatever type of storage is used, the computer has an advantage over the human being in that it can automatically recall within a few seconds or less whatever has been deposited in its memory, while a man may find himself unable to recall something he knows perfectly well. It would be a mistake, however, to conclude that an electronic memory is perfect. It may, however rarely, betray the fallibility of all created things, through false recordings, incomplete erasures, or other malfunctioning of its wonderful mechanisms.

People put up with the expense and complexity of computers for the same reason that an opera company puts up with a quarrelsome prima donna—because nobody else can do what she does. RCA's BIZMAC ($1,200,000 to $4,100,-000) keeps track of auto and tank inventory for the Army Ordnance Tank-Automotive Command. The physical inventory is scattered all over the world; BIZMAC's memory of it is on magnetic tape in Detroit. It takes in 200,000 types of spare parts, from nuts and bolts to whole engines. Records are kept up to date within 48 hours and the machine will answer any inquiry pertaining to its responsibilities within three minutes and print it at a speed of 600 lines a minute through one of a battery of 25 electric typewriters.

Such gargantuan exhibits are few, but an increasing number of computers of more modest size are revolutionizing—the word is hardly an exaggeration in this instance—many phases of ordinary business. Soldiers speak of the "fog" or confusion of battle and it is a fact that most business likewise has been carried on in a haze of uncertainty concerning inventories, sales, costs, production schedules, payrolls, etc., at the time when decisions had to be made.

Consider, for instance, that a textile converter who dyes
or prints cloth may have 8,000 different finished styles,
patterns, and color combinations, each of which may be
stocked in three different lengths or packagings, making
24,000 different stock items. These may be located at the
point of production or at warehouses, and each of the items
on a customer's order may happen to be at a different location. Consider also that this is a volatile business, and a
seasonal product which is not moving well may be sold
out by a prompt 5 per cent markdown, while a few months
hence even a 50 per cent markdown may not avail. Only a
computer can enable the converter to forecast the market,
control inventory and production, ship goods promptly,
remain constantly informed on lagging and runaway items,
and in general run his business in a businesslike manner.

Any number of other applications in the most diverse
enterprises can be cited. Coded time cards can be fed
into a computer, and associated machinery and employees'
pay statements and paychecks taken out at the other end,
after calculations for half a dozen withholding items, over-
time, etc. The largest payrolls can be handled in this
fashion in a fraction of the time and with a fraction of the
personnel required with the best pre-electronic systems.
Then there are the check-processing machines like the
Bank of America's ERMA (*Electronic Recording Machine
—Accounting*) which scans a canceled check for the de-
positor's code number (printed in magnetic ink on the
back), deducts the amount from his balance, blinks a red
light if he is overdrawn, signals for stopped-payment

checks and other contingencies, and at the end of the month prints his statement from the accumulated data. Each of the forthcoming ERMA models will handle 50,000 accounts and the Bank of America, with 6 million depositors, expects to electronize a major part of its operations.

Less sensational than the big brains and special machines, but scarcely less important in the aggregate, are the modest $32,500 to $49,500 computers (including one-year service and parts warranty) such as the Burroughs E101, Royal McBee LPG-30, Underwood ELECOM 50, or Bendix Aviation G-15. These desk-size machines rent for $850 to $1,485 per month, and even if you are a big corporation with a big computer, it may pay you to get one of

these "small-scale" jobs. In the December 1955 *Proceedings* of the Radio Club of America, James L. Rogers tells of the savage intracorporate struggles which a single large computer may give rise to. The trusting engineer comes to the programmers with a problem and is turned down on the ground that it isn't complex enough. After repeated experience of this sort he learns how to swindle his way into the computer: instead of the three-digit accuracy he needs, he asks for eight digits, instead of results every two degrees, he asks for every fortieth of a degree, etc. It takes him some time to dig what he really needs out of the mass of data the computer showers on him, but still he is far ahead compared with manual computation. But give him a desk-size machine to fill the gap between the slide rule and the giant brain, and he is happy without tying up the far more expensive machine.

You can even get a kit and assemble your own computer. The Heath Company of Benton Harbor, Michigan, sells computer kits (besides other electronic kits) for between $945 and $1,550. These are *analogue* machines, to be distinguished from the digital machines we have been discussing. The digital type deals with abstract numbers, the analogue type with physical quantities. Watt's steam-engine governor is an analogue machine; so is the speedometer of your automobile, in which the movement of a pointer over a dial is proportional to the revolution of the wheels. The "analogue" comes in because the system simulates or expresses results proportional to the behavior of another system under study, the underlying mathematics being the same. Modern analogue computers are largely assemblies of electronic circuits which behave like their mechanical or electrical counterparts. If the Heath product is wired at a university, the students end up with considerable knowledge of computer anatomy (and soldering) and the university ends up with a computer.

The Electronic Library   Obviously information-processing and communication machines can be used by librarians as well as airlines and banks, and in fact there is a great deal of activity going on along these lines. W. H. MacWilliams Jr. writes in the February, 1953, issue of *Electrical Engineering* that information "is being accumulated far faster than it is being read, and the days in which a person could consider himself fully conversant with the developments in even a single field have long since passed. Specialized work is essential for progress, but it is equally essential to make it readily available." MacWilliams points out that the digital computer, with its capacious memory, may be the answer. Pioneering efforts in this field have included a machine devised by Vannevar Bush and Ralph Shaw. Bush, who has played a leading role in computer technology and American technology generally for many years, records printed matter in random order on microfilm. The informational content of each frame is described on the margin in 12 words ("descriptors") recorded in binary code. A photocell can scan the film at a speed of about 5,000 words per minute, and when a pertinent frame is found the machine makes a duplicate, which can then be read in the usual optical enlarger.

This system can quickly accumulate a large volume of material on a subject, but the value of the descriptors is limited by the learning and imagination of the indexer. His lapses may result in the loss of valuable collateral ideas, or even of central concepts. It remains to be seen whether the system will give rise to those fresh and original ideas which are so often the product of chance, indirect suggestion, and reverie. It may be that for purposes of invention both the conventional and new methods of research will prove useful.

Language Machines Modern technology has outgrown human translation of one language into another. William N. Locke of the Massachusetts Institute of Technology, primarily a linguist, in an article, "Translation by Machine" in the January, 1956, *Scientific American,* cites a scientific paper to show how important translation is. The title of the paper is "The Application of Boolean Matrix Algebra to the Analysis and Synthesis of Relay Contact Networks." Published in 1950, it had a direct bearing on a number of practical problems in communications. But it happened to be published in the *Journal of the USSR Academy of Sciences.* Although the *Journal* was freely available in the United States, for five frustrating and costly years American scientists and engineers failed to find solutions to questions which were cleared up in this paper. To make the situation more ludicrous, George Boole (1815–1864) was an Englishman. It's just that very few Americans read Russian. If as few Russians read English, that is our good luck—but the Boolean case doesn't look much like it.

Translation by human translators isn't the answer, or at any rate not the whole answer. Just to speak of translation is almost meaningless. A translator capable of doing a first-rate job on a Russian novel might be helpless with the paper on Boolean algebra. To translate physics, Locke points out, you practically have to be a physicist: it may be added that in engineering, you might have to be a particular kind of engineer. And where do you put the few qualified men to work on the mass of material which should be screened? Machinery, fast, tireless, seems to be the only solution.

It does not need to be a perfect machine, nor can anything approaching perfection be expected in the immediate future, especially in dealing with the more difficult languages, such as Russian and Chinese, which, from a military or paramilitary standpoint, are the urgent ones. The practical solution would seem to be a machine which can translate from Russian into a kind of pidgin English which might then be rearranged into acceptable scientific English. For ambiguous passages, in large organizations a human translator could be on tap to assist the machine.

The nature of the machine-translation problem is illustrated by a story told by Warren Weaver, Vice President for the Natural and Medical Sciences of the Rockefeller

Foundation. The story was first published in Weaver's memorandum on "Translation," privately circulated in 1949 and reprinted in *Machine Translation of Languages* (1955), edited by Locke and A. Donald Booth, a British computer expert. During World War II a distinguished ex-German mathematician, whom Weaver identifies only as *P*, was asked by a colleague who was an amateur cryptographer to draft a coded message which the colleague would try to decipher. *P* happened to have spent some time at the University of Istanbul, so he wrote a message of 100 words in Turkish and transposed it into five-digit code. The colleague did not know Turkish and had no idea what language had been used for the original message. The next day he brought back his results to *P* with the remark that his attempt to break *P*'s code had apparently failed, because the decoded version made no sense. But, with some unimportant corrections, the decoded version was the original message, and anybody who knew Turkish could read it.

At first it may seem that all that had happened was that the amateur cryptographer had broken the code, and should have been in some cryptographic division of the armed services. But there is much more to it than that. Codes are broken by noting frequencies of letters, letter combinations, recurring patterns, possible stereotypes, etc. For this reason military messages are customarily garbled in the plain language original, stereotypes are avoided, and all normal beginnings are buried in the body of the message. But in the case cited by Weaver the cryptographer retrieved the message without knowing the language. Weaver surmised that there must be invariant properties common to all languages, which would be natural enough since all men have basically the same vocal organs and nervous systems. The invariant properties are not, of course, by any means identical; their resemblances are only statistically significant. But if so, a computer should be able to translate, once the common elements have been found and used to instruct it.

The computer does not work merely as a rapid dictionary: the problem is far more complex than that. It must also be able to work on the basis of context, word order, idiom, etc. The problems are, in fact, akin to the problems of cryptography, as Weaver understood from the outset. Seeing a Russian article, he thought, "This is really written in English, but it has been coded in some strange symbols. I will now proceed to decode."

It follows that a computer in the hands of a skilled cryptographer should be able to break any existing code, but the opposite is also true: by the use of computers it should be possible to devise more complex codes which it will take even smarter computers to break, and so on ad infinitum.

What of the future? Several writers have written books full of synthetic panic about the robots who are about to take over the affairs of mankind. Mankind is in more danger from itself than from its robots, but there is no doubt that the computer will play an increasingly important part

in human affairs, probably for good, but whether for good
or for evil it is too early to say. Computers that can modify
their behavior in accordance with statistical or other experience, thus becoming capable of learning, are conceivable and, being conceivable, will be made. Computers
have been interconnected (by the National Bureau of
Standards), a master controlling a slave machine and the
two sharing a single problem. So we can visualize a hier-
archy of computers running the mechanized aspects of a
business, with an executive machine directing the activities
of subordinate machines responsible for departmental
operation. It is coming: in some phases it is already here.

Even more ambitious projects have been suggested.
W. W. Leontief and others believe that computers will be
used for general economic analysis and forecasting. W.
Ross Ashby has gone farther and proposed an "intelligence
amplifier," arguing that if physical energy can be amplified, as it is in every radio and television receiver, the
same can be done for intelligence. "There is certainly no
lack of difficult problems awaiting solution," Ashby points
out. ". . . It is perhaps in the social and economic world
that such problems occur most noticeably, both in regard
to their complexity and to the great issues that depend on
them. Success in solving these problems is a matter of
some urgency. We have built a civilization beyond our
understanding and we are finding that it is getting out of
hand. Faced with such problems, what are we to do?"

But it is not essentially a matter of understanding.
Limited as human intelligence is, there is enough of it to

solve these problems if it could be freely applied and if people were really interested in reaching solutions. The problems are no more complicated than the people who make them. But as long as animosity, spontaneous or contrived, is the order of the day, how can agreement be reached on the premises to be fed into the machine? How many professional social scientists, even, make any serious effort to evaluate the work of their predecessors—Ricardo, Marx, Engels, Adam Smith, Keynes, Malthus, Veblen, and the many other big and controversial names of the social sciences—and to separate the seminal contributions from the failures? If natural scientists and engineers were as prejudiced and timid in their specialties as most social scientists, not to speak of politicians and publicists, are in theirs, either the progress of the steam engine would have stopped with James Watt, or the respectable history books would mention him only to condemn him for his error in not employing high-pressure steam. It will take more than a computer to change this.

Including the Kitchen Sink

Miscellaneous Business The disparity of the applications not yet mentioned shows how deeply automation has already permeated modern life and gives an inkling of what is to come: Automatic vending machines are assuming an ever-increasing role in retail trade. Everyone knows that a modern war could not be fought without soft-drink machines to energize the civilian and military personnel

at bases all over the world. Somewhere or other almost everything is sold by machine except contraceptives and firearms. In the New York subways, directions for travel are handed out by a machine. The main New York post office has a stamp-vending machine which is on duty 24 hours a day, and, after each sale, intones sweetly, "Thank you. These stamps are sanitary." . . . Tolls are collected on the New Jersey Garden State Parkway by a machine, provided the motorist has 25 cents in coin; otherwise he must drive up to a human toll collector. . . . Ernest Henderson, the farsighted president of the Sheraton hotel chain, predicts room-service orders via TV, luggage conveyers replacing bell hops, electronic systems of check-in and check-out. . . . An official of Minneapolis-Honeywell bawled out dairymen for not using automation enough. Properly instrumented with, say, Minneapolis-Honeywell instruments, including a special-purpose computer, such plants could establish the butter-fat content of the milk, do the accounting and keep the records, and write a check for the farmer almost as soon as he had delivered the milk.

The "Auto-typist" of the American Automatic Typewriter Company is used in direct-mail promotion and other business correspondence for producing form letters which are indistinguishable from dictated letters and cost less. It is a pneumatically-powered servomechanism which will operate any typewriter, manual or electric, at a speed some 2½ times that of normal professional typing. Form letters or paragraphs are composed and recorded on a paper roll similar to that of a player piano. An electric switching mechanism selects the desired prerecorded paragraphs, and also permits the operator to type in the recipient's name and address and to interpolate special material, such as a caressing repetition of the recipient's name, references to model numbers, cities, dates, etc. It is a useful machine for complaint departments, for example, or for imparting "a mechanical pat on the back," as in sending birthday and anniversary greetings to customers. Other suggestions include, for schools and universities, fund-raising letters to alumni; for banks, stimulating inactive accounts and soliciting installment loan business; for publishers, rejection letters; and—AAT is not responsible for this one—personalized letters to a lady, or ladies, from a busy lover.

Sports According to the New York *Times* of November 25, 1956, the digital computer has been used successfully to predict the result of a football game. It seems that Mr. Bob Wyckoff, head of the University of Pittsburgh's news service, accompanied by Mr. Carroll (Beano) Cook, sports public-relations director, were concerned about the outcome of an impending game with Penn State. Accordingly they hastened to the United States Steel building in Pittsburgh, where it is possible that they met a publicity man for US Steel and perhaps also one for International Business Machines, for it was a Type 650 IBM computer on the US Steel premises that was chosen as the instrument of divination. The data fed into the machine included the speed of the halfbacks, the weight and speed of the linemen, the past performances of the teams, and even the number of years the head coaches had served in their high offices. The electrons whirled and the computer printed the figure "one" for each side. The publicity men were naturally puzzled, until the programmer explained that the machine probably meant that the game would be a tie, with each team scoring once. And indeed, the final score of the contest, witnessed by 51,123 persons, was 7-7.

And the IBM 650 is only an intermediate-size machine, not even a "giant brain"!

The Arts In the early decades of the century the player piano utilized Jacquard's punched cards in the form of a paper roll to control the hammers by a pneumatic servo-mechanism. We have come a long way since then. Some musicians, especially in West Germany (the "Cologne school") believe that the future of music lies in the realm of electronics. They record music on tapes, using electronic tone generators, and have abandoned conventional musical notation for the language of electrical engineering, duration being expressed in fractions of an inch of tape, diminuendos and crescendos in decibels. Professor Meyer Eppler of the University of Bonn is quoted as saying that "a composer will be able to fix his ideas forever in sound through electronic devices, just as a sculptor fixes his ideas in modeling clay. No interpretation or change will be possible later."

It is too early to predict when and to what extent machines will come into use for practical composition, but the engineers are doing their damnedest. There are also plans on foot for synthesizing speech by a similar technique. It would seem possible to alter a recording to make a speaker say the opposite of what he actually said, or to simulate his voice electronically and make a recording not one word of which was actually uttered by him. Not content with tapping your wires and recording what you said, "they" will record what you didn't say.

No serious suggestions have yet been made for the automation of painting and sculpture, but it is worth noting that both James Watt and Robert Fulton worked on ideas for mechanizing sculpture. Watt's contribution was a dimension-transferring machine for reproducing a human head. He thought it would replace freehand sculpture. It didn't, but it would be rash to assume that modern automation will not affect the last refuges of individual self-expression.

R & D are the magic initials in modern industry. They stand for Research and Development, the source of the flood of new and profitable products which helps to sustain prosperity. But R & D, as now conducted, is a slow process from gestation in the mind of the inventor, to drafting and handmade parts for a "breadboard" prototype, which, after testing and evaluation, points the way to the drafting, design, tooling, testing, debugging, and mass production of a salable product.

There have been a number of proposals for short-circuiting this process. One of them, by George R. Price in the November, 1956 *Fortune,* involves producing a 3-D image of parts of a model by means of a computer and television screens, testing it electronically, and "autofacturing" * a physical model by feeding data from the computer to a multipurpose machine tool. Price believes that by speeding up R & D in this fashion, the 3 per cent average annual increase in the rate of productivity might be raised to 4–5 per cent at a possible cost of $5–6 billion a year which, he points out, is being spent annually on national advertising alone.

This scheme, as yet only on paper, sounds less fantastic to the engineer than to the layman. To a certain extent it is already being done. Instead of building a prototype of a jet engine at a cost of $10 million or more, and even more precious time, the engineers can construct it mathematically and flight-test it in a mathematical airplane, by using a computer. If there is anything wrong, the computer will reveal it. When they find a combination which "flies" better than other mathematical models, the manufacturers proceed to a physical prototype. It would be too much to expect that the prototype will fly in the air exactly as its

* An apt term suggested by Emil J. Simon, one of the pioneers of radio in the United States.

mathematical predecessor flew in the computer, but it is certainly a less expensive way of going about the development job.

From Hippocrates to Zworykin   Hippocrates ("Father of Medicine" c. 460–377 B.C.) was a physician. Vladimir K. Zworykin (1889–) is an engineer, an honorary vice president of the Radio Corporation of America. But the two disciplines are not as far apart as they used to be. Zworykin, largely responsible for modern television, has made considerable contributions to the Hippocratic art and is on the way to making more.

Many great advances in medicine have involved the application of chemistry, physics, and engineering to the problems of medicine, whether by physicians or others. We have only to think of Laënnec's invention of the stethoscope, Einthoven and the string galvanometer, and G. W. Crile's great work on surgical shock after World War I. These three were physicians who picked up what they needed from other branches of technology. Einthoven, not finding what he wanted, made a bold excursion into electrical engineering and not only cleared the way for the electrocardiograph but for modern oscillography. In the other direction, Röntgen's x-rays were seized on for medical radiography almost as soon as he discovered them.

But, as Zworykin points out, in such complex fields as medicine and biology it is becoming more and more difficult to apply the results of research in other fields. No physician can know all of medicine, much less of physics; no physicist can know much of medicine. The only solution is for teams of specialists to work together on the most urgent problems. That is being done, although not nearly as much as would be desirable. The Institute of Radio Engineers has a Professional Group on Medical Electronics, the American Institute of Electrical Engineers has its Committee on Electrical Techniques in Medicine and Biology, the Rockefeller Institute has its Medical Electronics Center. Among the results so far are the employment of color television in surgery and the linkage of television with x-ray observation and therapy, the electron microscope and the television microscope, electronic sanguinometers or blood-cell counting and measuring devices, the applications of various types of radiation meters and counters, the oximeter which measures the oxygen carried by the blood, blood flowmeters, amplifiers which detect the minutest electrical potentials within the body, cardiac monitors, and other devices too numerous to itemize. Many of these instruments operate with a considerable degree of automaticity, and the outright application of automation to medicine is a future possibility.

Essentially the physician is a service man for the human body. Since the body is appallingly complicated, the physician has even less chance of making the right diagnosis without instruments than a television service man would have without his signal generators, tube testers, and oscilloscopes. For the same reason it takes longer and costs more to train a doctor than any other technologist, and his training must continue throughout life. It is therefore of the utmost importance to utilize his services to the best advantage during the forty or fifty years in which he and society must amortize the investment. This is being done very poorly for a number of reasons, one of which is that the physician tries to do manually a great many things which in every other field of technology are done more or less automatically. A high-quality physical examination, for instance, even when done by a team of specialists, may require several days of testing and analysis. Moreover, as preventive medicine comes abreast of preventive maintenance in less important fields, there will have to be more frequent and more exhaustive examinations of more people—of the whole population, in fact, for human beings, after all, are our most important product. Still another defect in the present medical technology is the fact that readings of the various vital parameters, such as heart action, temperature, and blood pressure are not taken simultaneously, which tends to obscure the correlations. Such a disparate system of measurement would never be tolerated in, for instance, an oil refinery.

Zworykin's proposal is that these variables be recorded on a single piece of electronic equipment operated *by a technician.* The design of such a multiple-purpose instrument would probably entail no greater difficulty than the design of an electron microscope, for instance, and its operation would require no more skill than taking electrocardiograms, which even now is frequently done by a trained nurse. The data so secured would be entered with readings of weight, body dimensions, etc., on punched cards and would provide a permanent, easily scanned record of the patient's condition. As it is now, the physician scrawls figures and observations on cards, wasting his time in recording and again whenever he refers to what he has written—if he is able to read it.

Ultimately, Zworykin suggests, the information could be fed into a computer "which would have stored in its memory the best medical knowledge of the day," and the machine would come up with a diagnosis. If this seems far-fetched, at least the machine could indicate whether further investigation was called for. Of course nobody is suggesting that the machine would substitute for a physician. It would, on the contrary, enable him to spend his time doing what only he can do. After the machine had prepared the ground, the physician would apply his clinical sense, size up the patient's personality, reassure him if necessary, and do all the other personal therapeutic things required. Not only could the physician carry a larger case load with less strain, but the cost of medical care, which has risen steadily as medicine has become more and more technological, might be brought back to a range within the means of middle-class patients.

A number of special-purpose automatic medical instruments were described at the 1956 convention of the Instrument Society of America, one by Alan G. Slocombe of Tufts College, under the title of "An Electronic Servo-anesthetizer." It is based on a system devised by Dr. G. Bickford of the Mayo Clinic. Anesthesia is conventionally

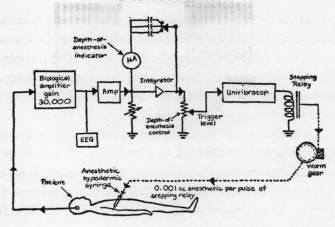

regulated in accordance with the anesthetist's observations of heart and respiratory action, reflexes, eye movements, etc., and his evaluation of how much anesthetic the patient needs and can stand. Another factor, which cannot be directly observed, is the electrical activity of the brain. By means of the electroencephalograph, which is the cerebral counterpart of the electrocardiograph, the brain waves can be amplified and displayed on graph paper. The curve drops under anesthesia. This relationship suggests that the brain signal may be used to control the depth of anesthesia automatically. The anesthetist could then let the machine administer the anesthetic and intervene only when he saw some indication that the optimum level was not being maintained.

So far this ingenious system has been used only on rats. If the relationship between the brain waves and depth of anesthesia can be accurately established for a variety of surgical situations, it may be applied to human beings. It is conceivable that an anesthetist could cover two operations going on simultaneously in the same or adjoining rooms in this manner. One patient might be undergoing some routine operation like a simple appendectomy; he would require only an occasional glance by the anesthetist while a nurse would watch blood pressure and other readings; the servoanesthetizer would do the rest. The other operation might be difficult or involve a patient who was a poor surgical risk; here the anesthetist would closely supervise the machine or perhaps disable the servomechanism and control the input of anesthetic manually.

Machines designed along such lines could conceivably transfer the routine jobs of surgical practice to echelons of hospital workers below the specialist and MD level and conserve the time of specialists and the highly trained. This seems imperative and indeed such a trend is already manifest, for the number of physicians relative to population has been decreasing over the last five decades; at the same time there has been a marked increase in the medical subprofessions. It is another setup for automation, and probably the most important of all.

CHAPTER 5

Automation and the Boom

THERE ARE always those who, scanning the indicators and auspices of the vast economic machine, find it proof against any evil visitation. If they should be right this time, automation will be necessary to satisfy the demand for goods. If they turn out to be wrong and the current boom goes the way of its predecessors, automation will be the indispensable weapon in the battle for markets. After the first shock wears off, the progress of automation is bound to be accelerated in the transition from a buoyant economy to one in which hope and fear are intermingled. In a depression, automation investment would be less expensive than it is under boom conditions, and hence still more attractive to astute businessmen.

A rise in business investment would be therapeutic while it lasted, but then employment would resume its drop as the automated machinery went into operation. This amounts to saying that the cure for unemployment is more unemployment. And so it is—for the firms that win out in the cost-cutting struggle. In depressions, price reductions, which are largely theoretical during prosperity, become an imperative reality. Capturing a larger share of the market, the automated corporations will be able to stay in business—with reduced profits to be sure, but they will ride out the storm.

If this is carried through rapidly enough, automation could blow up a mere recession into a full-scale depression, for then, and only then, will the savings of automation be passed on to the consumers, but the only consumers it will be possible to pass them on to will be those who still have money and confidence, i.e., those who will need them least. The people out of work, or scared, will not be buying much. These crippled consumers will, at precisely the wrong time, be trying to save.

But if the situation should deteriorate to this extent

the government will intervene. There will never be another administration like that of President Hoover which tried, in effect, to sit out its depression. Both in terms of domestic politics and the international contest between communism and capitalism, a depression of the depth and duration of 1929–1941 (in 1941 there was still 10 per cent unemployment) is a very remote possibility. If it actually threatens, political means will be used to arrest it. In this connection, the last thing to lose sight of is the fact that the current boom is significantly sustained by military spending.

The present effect of the new technology, with its massive military component, is to prolong the boom. Without it, corporate directors might already have cut back new fixed investments, for although output of manufactured goods has been rising rapidly since World War II, manufacturing capacity has been rising even faster and excess capacity, even when not very large, is always a brake on expansion. But the new technology has not only induced businessmen to continue to invest, but to increase their commitments inordinately. Another bullish item is industrial research, said to be running at an annual rate of $5.5 billion, a sum which by itself, let alone the marketable products it is creating, is helping to maintain prosperity, or at any rate to postpone the day of reckoning.

Still another favorable factor is that the strongest and most solidly financed corporations, which are for the most part also the largest, are now planning on a relatively long-term basis and seem less inclined to cut back appropriations for capital expenditures because of intervening fluctuations. Of course they can always change their minds; business judgment is largely the faculty of changing one's mind at the right point in the business cycle. If, however, they continue steadfast, that in itself would tend to hold fluctuations within narrower limits than heretofore. Advanced automation will tend to reinforce this tendency, since it involves the planning and integration of the whole enterprise, from raw materials to marketing —but that is still some distance in the future.

In the competition of large versus small business, automation will increase the advantages already enjoyed by big business. This is not a matter of technology: many small concerns can automate successfully and some are doing so. A drill and reamer manufacturer is quoted in the *Wall Street Journal* (July 5, 1956): "Automation is our salvation. It has helped us to triple production and carve a spot in a highly competitive industry." But such cases will probably turn out to be exceptional. Much small business is undercapitalized and in chronic financial straits. When the cost of borrowing is raised to control inflation, it has little effect on borrowers in the prime classification, but in a tight money market the small businessman may not be able to borrow at all. "The larger companies," says a market letter on automation issued by Bache & Company, a Wall Street investment house, "are obviously in the best position to develop and finance research, production and marketing." Indeed, technological progress and efficiency is largely a matter of having

APPLICATION FOR EMPLOYMENT

WRITE KIND OF WORK WANTED
1. Engineer
2.
3.

PRINT NAME: DA VINCI, LEONARDO

LAST • FIRST • MIDDLE • SOCIAL SECURITY NO.

DATE

STREET ADDRESS • CITY • ZONE • STATE • NEAREST PHONE

HOME	CHECK WHICH	MARITAL	CHECK WHICH	PHYSICAL
OWN HOME		SINGLE	✓	SEX
RENT HOME		MARRIED		DRAFT STATUS
RENT ROOM		WIDOW		HEIGHT
BOARD		WIDOWER		WEIGHT
LIVE WITH		SEPARATED		COLOR HAIR
PARENTS		DIVORCED		COLOR EYES

DATE OF BIRTH
ARE YOU A CITIZEN OF USA?
FATHER'S NAME .... Occupation
WHICH PARENTS ARE LIVING
Name of husband or wife .... On
Number of children under 18 years
Number of additional dependents

RESIDENT OF STATE SINCE

MILITARY SERVICE

FROM .... TO
BRANCH .... RANK
PROMOTIONS
INJURIES

IN CASE OF EMERGENCY NOTIFY
NAME .... RELAT.
ST.
CITY & STATE
NEAREST PHONE

RECORD OF BUSINESS EXPERIENCE

FROM - TO	NAME OF COMPANY (Show Present Position First)	ADDRESS
1	Engineering	
2	Architecture	
3	Painting	
4	Chemistry	
5	Physics	

On what office .... Sculpture
Dictation speed .... City Planning .... Typing spe

EDUCATIONAL RECO

KIND	"Military"	DATES ATT. FROM—TO	YEARS CREDIT	DEGREE
GRADE	Sanitary Engineering			
HIGH	Agriculture			
COLLEGE	Poetry			
TECH.	Aviation			
OTHER				

Applicant Do Not Write Below This Line

REMARKS BY INTERVIEWER

Approved for Employment

money. With money one can buy the best equipment, hire the best engineers, conduct lucrative research and write off the losses in research that doesn't pan out—and cover up one's errors. There is first-class engineering talent in some small organizations and these may succeed despite financial handicaps, but the road is getting rougher as technology becomes more complex. This is true everywhere, not only in the United States. Dr. Alexander King, a British authority on automation, points out that it is most easily adopted by "the larger and more progressive firms in those industries which were expanding and were originally science-based." And, he might have added, well-heeled, for these qualities go together.

Another factor militating against small firms in the United States is the accelerated amortization or "fast write-off" program. This permits corporations—preponderantly large ones—to write off in five years, instead of the customary twenty, facilities needed for military purposes. As a result the profits and financial condition of these large corporations, usually already quite healthy, wax even more exuberant. For instance, the Pennsylvania Railroad was able to cut its 1955 Federal income taxes from $9,026,047 to $1,608,047 by fast write-offs on rolling stock and other facilities, and in 1954, 1953, and 1952 the road benefited even more substantially. Secretary of the Treasury George M. Humphrey has said that the accelerated amortization program cost the government some $880 million in tax revenue during the fiscal year of 1956. Even if the practice is discontinued in the near future,

APPLICATION FOR EMPLOYMENT

WRITE KIND OF WORK WANTED
1 *Engineer*

DA VINCI, LEONARDO

RECORD OF BUSINESS EXPERIENCE

Engineering
Architecture
Painting
Chemistry
Physics
Sculpture
City Planning
Military
Sanitary Engineering
Agriculture
Poetry
Aviation

Application rejected!
Applicant has too many
side interests!!

the damage, so far as small business is concerned, has already been done. Enough excess plant has been built up in some industries—largely at the small taxpayers' expense—to supply both the military and civilian markets. Small business in these fields must compete with new plants and facilities with a total cost, up to the fall of 1956, of almost $37 billion, of which 61 per cent, or $22.5 billion, was covered by "certificates of necessity."

The Bache letter previously cited, referring to companies engaged in manufacturing instrumentation and automation equipment, says: "If history is any guide, as competition intensifies many companies will disappear through absorption by larger enterprises, merger with other concerns, abandonment or even bankruptcy." This may be true not only of specialized automation concerns, but of business generally under the impact of automation, where, for instance, an unautomated product may be forced out of the market by a substitute susceptible of automation. If so, it will merely accelerate a process al-

ready well under way. Holding-company control of widely diversified industry is spreading so rapidly that newspaper financial sections devote a daily column to mergers, which are not confined to corporations of the same species but include matings unparalleled outside of Greek mythology. It surprises no one, nowadays, to hear that a housewares manufacturer has become a division of a corporation operating drydocks and wrecking tugs, any more than it is surprising to find the controlling stockholder of the latter waging a proxy fight to get control of a mail-order house. Automation technique and automation experts will at least supply a measure of functional liaison between concerns which are now linked only through their balance sheets and a faith in the magical efficacy of management regardless of knowledge or lack of knowledge of the things being managed. Actually, a great deal of this much-touted quality of managerial judgment is mere speculative hunch and daring, which automatically succeed in a bull market but contribute to the failures and suicides in a bear market.

The consumer's stake in automation, again under the conditions of the boom, is nothing to get excited about. This applies particularly to the consumer who is most in need of help, not only for his sake, but for everybody's. Capitalism on the American plan has materially expanded and improved the lot of the middle class. Secretary Humphrey points with pride to the fact that where, early in the century, only ten out of a hundred families earned as much as $4,000 a year in 1955 dollars, in 1955 fifty-five out of a hundred did so. This is a valid argument and not to be minimized in evaluations of the strength and viability of the free-enterprise system. But it is also true that in 1955 one out of five families, comprising thirty million Americans, had incomes of less than $2,000, and the top tenth—these figures are as pertinent as they are familiar—owned 65 per cent of all family-held liquid assets, while the bottom four-tenths owned less than 1 per cent.

Automation may further increase the wealth of the upper strata. It may leave the middle strata unchanged, or somewhat improve their condition. But what of the lower strata? They are the crucial ones. The fact is that an advanced technological society can no longer afford poverty. Poverty isn't the Achilles heel of the American economy; it is gangrene of the whole foot. But the bottom fifth will be the least benefited by automation, since it consists of the actually unemployable, those regarded as unemployable, and those whom it would be most expensive to upgrade.

The weakness of capitalism, even of American capitalism, is in the organs of circulation or distribution. In production it has done and is doing a pretty good job, in some fields a brilliant job. In so far as automation is an improvement, or complex of improvements, in production, it cannot help to solve the central problem of capitalism. The economy has never utilized the resources of its technology to the fullest extent, not even in wartime. Automation may increase the pressures in the direction of full utilization, but under the conditions of the boom these cannot be effective: the purchasing power is lacking. In a depression it is even more lacking.

Intelligent capitalists are of course aware of the underlying difficulty, although they usually discuss it only in terms of obstacles to selling. Thus Dr. W. R. G. Baker, for many years vice president in charge of electronics for General Electric, refers to figures showing that in some industries distribution takes one to two out of every ten product dollars, in some three or four, while in still others distribution costs are many times the factory cost of the product. Distribution costs, moreover, have been on the rise. Obviously, in such cases, when you reduce the factory cost, whether by automation or hypnosis, you have not taken much of a step toward the goal of pouring a flood of inexpensive goods into the consumer's lap.

Even with present plant there are no important shortages in consumers' goods, which means that this plant, although not yet radically affected by automation, is producing all that the market can absorb even while pressing consumer credit to its safe limits, if not beyond. In the present market, therefore, automation is not an urgent necessity. True, if the market can be sufficiently enlarged, existing surplus capacity can be put to work and additional capacity generated by automation can be absorbed. But measures to enlarge the market normally take the form of strategy to grab a larger share of the consumer's dollar, and ignore the basic difficulty that he hasn't enough dollars to spend.

Viewed realistically, the prospect is that business will

resort to higher-pressure selling, larger advertising appropriations, bigger expense accounts for top salesmen, more spectacular (but not necessarily more esthetic) remodeling, and that automation will be utilized mainly to pay for the increased costs involved in this sort of sales strategy. But how will that benefit the consumer, even if the strategy succeeds?

Also: let's not overlook the steady growth in monopoly practices and in price-fixing at the wholesale level since World War II. It is probably not without significance that the industry which is in the most advanced stage of automation at the present time—the petroleum industry—is notoriously addicted to price-fixing, and that this exploitation of the consumer is legally sanctioned by the governments of oil-producing states, while the federal government polices these regulations in interstate commerce. Further automation will change none of this.

There may be spot depressions or recessions within a boom; we have seen them in the past few years in television, appliances, the movies, textiles, home-building, even in automobiles. In some of these cases prices will drop. But as long as the boom lasts the vision of a general lowering of the cost of living, through automation or any other means, is a will-o'-the-wisp. Prices can drop generally only in a general depression.

Automation may be the salvation of a particular enterprise, but it cannot stabilize the free-enterprise economy as a whole—rather the contrary. Certain assumptions are casually made by many of the promoters of automation which, if true, would insure an indefinite continuance of prosperity. But they are not true. The key postulate is that effective demand must somehow keep pace with productivity. Even trade-union leaders talk of a "balance" between rising output and purchasing power as automation takes hold. But there is no such balance now. Since the balance doesn't exist and nothing is being done to achieve it by increasing mass purchasing power, how can we talk of it as a prospective condition? And does anyone seriously doubt that automation will make it harder to achieve?

If the economy is really in a healthy state, why are so many of its putative beneficiaries in hock? Dependence on consumer debt will in no wise be altered by automation

or other technological advances, however brilliant. Dr. Elmer W. Engstrom, senior executive vice president of the Radio Corporation of America and an engineer well-versed in automation, puts it this way: "High productivity by itself can become a liability when the consumer is not interested in buying." Or is unable to buy. Or has been buying at 15 per cent interest not through loan sharks, but through the most respectable institutions, until the time comes when he can buy no more.

If the boom ends in this way, what then? What will probably happen is what is already happening, only more so. The beset economy will resort increasingly to military production and sales. Business can stop investing and consumers can stop buying, but government spending is controllable. And the one form of government spending which never encounters serious opposition is for armaments.

The electronics industry, closely meshed with automation, provides a crystal ball. With annual sales of $12 billion, it ranks fifth among American industries. *Fortune* (April, 1957) has diagrammed and labeled its history. Until the advent of radio broadcasting it could hardly qualify as an industry. Short-term gyrations being flattened out, it climbed slowly until the war gave it a powerful impetus through radar and other military developments. Radar was of great technological help to television, which took over for the next rise. But this civilian-fed boomlet lasted only four years. Radio and TV manufacturers today live in what *Fortune* calls a "mature, dangerous jungle," in which the big operators are forcing out the little ones. Out of 101

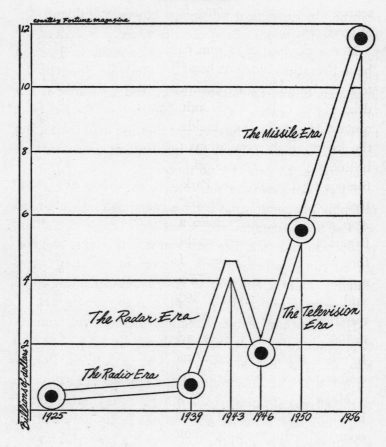

TV-receiver manufacturers still surviving in 1954, 51 have since quit, and the end is not yet. But in the meantime the electronic sales curve has kept on shooting up, with the military again taking over from the flagging civilian economy. With the armed services buying half the industry's product and providing a great proportion of its vital research it has indeed become, in *Fortune*'s caption, "a child of government."

Home electronics is one case where consumer prices have been reduced. But how? Let us see what happened to Avco Manufacturing Company, high in the second hundred of the largest U. S. industrial corporations. The sequence of events may incidentally cast some doubt on the long-term extrapolations so generally engaged in by business leaders nowadays. At the 1955 Boston Conference on Distribution, Parker H. Erickson, then executive vice president of Avco's Crosley and Bendix Home Appliance Divisions (radio and television receivers, refrigerators and freezers, washers and dryers, ranges, etc.), forecast a "growth picture" for business in general and appliances in particular. "Today's American family," he said, "has approximately $630.00 annually to spend on durable goods. But the 1960 family will have $750.00 and in 1965, 56 million families each will have $900.00 to spend. In other words, 20 per cent more families will have 50 per cent more money to spend in this area."

Maybe so, but Avco's not going to get any of it. Victor Emanuel, chairman and president of Avco, explained in an open letter to Avco stockholders, published in the New York *Times* for October 30, 1956, why Avco was discontinuing manufacture of Crosley and Bendix consumer products. "The appliance industry is plagued with large over-capacities," Mr. Emanuel said, "and has been rampant with price-cutting despite rising costs. . . . Your management . . . has carefully weighed whether future possibilities would warrant a large expenditure of capital funds necessary to meet competition by investing in very large plants with a high degree of automation." What he was referring to was General Electric's $156-million appliance plant at Louisville, Kentucky. Avco would have had, more or less, to match that investment. It wouldn't or couldn't.

So far as its Crosley and Bendix consumer products were concerned, Avco decided to die rather than automate. But condolences were not in order. There was another jungle, a benign one, in which Avco could live, and live well. Avco had a backlog of some $340 million in defense operations.

So far there have not been many cases of this magnitude, but Avco's is not the only one. When, on top of other reverses, the Studebaker-Packard Corporation lost the bulk of its defense contracts, it found itself in virtual bankruptcy and was saved from reorganization in the courts, or liquidation, only by what amounted to a forced sale of its assets, including a tax loss of $150 million, to the Curtiss-Wright Corporation, which then proceeded to transfer to the Studebaker-Packard plants $400 million in defense contracts of its own.

In the mixed-economy welfare state of Great Britain, at its present level of man-hour output or even at a higher automated level, full employment could readily be sustained without armaments; in fact, a capitalist economy in the condition of Great Britain's cannot afford heavy armament spending. But American experience since about the middle of the Great Depression holds out no such hope for the United States, possessed of a productive plant unmatched in history, undamaged by war and reaching for ever higher levels of output. Nor do American businessmen appear inclined to try the experiment. Since President Truman undertook the defense of Turkey and Greece against communism in 1947, military spending has been referred to in Wall Street as "underwriting" the boom, and so far it has proved to be very good insurance indeed.

Insurance of some sort is necessary, certainly. Military spending accounts for about 10 per cent of gross national product. At least 10 per cent of labor, therefore, or over seven million, is directly employed in the production of economic waste. If military expenditures should drop to the level of 1939 and nothing else happened in the economy, we could have our present output of consumer goods and services with over 10 million unemployed. Advancing automation could have the same effect.

In the past, since our own Civil War, war could give a boost to new branches of technology and the reinforced technologies could reciprocate by helping to lift the national economy to new heights. This happened with automobiles and radio in and after World War I, and with radio (which includes radar and television), nuclear energy, and automation in and after World War II. But although automation is playing some part in the boom of the Fifties and is destined to play a vastly larger part, and nuclear-explosives manufacture is presently the third largest industrial enterprise in the United States, outranked only by U. S. Steel and General Motors, the end-effects are quite different. Radio led the stock-market boom of the Twenties as a new consumer industry; in the boom of the Fifties we have seen how quickly it played itself out. Nuclear energy is injected into the economy via government spending, while automation is a new technique for business and industry. It can make goods more plentiful, by all indications too plentiful for an economy that already depends in such large measure on consumer debt and government subsidies.

If, as after 1933, 1942, and 1952, a large and probably permanent increase in federal spending should be called into play, must it take the form of military spending? Conceivably not, but the chances for welfare spending on a proportionate scale are slim, at least in the immediate future. Spending for welfare labors under severe political handicaps. For one thing, as Cavour said, it is easy to rule in a state of siege. Armament spending avails itself of the always ready testimony of high military officers and key legislators that the country is in peril. The business thus promoted goes mainly to large corporations. Since most of this military hardware is obsolescent by the time it is delivered, a continuous stream of defense orders is assured. Welfare spending is often suggested as a substitute for military spending, but the two are not economically equivalent. Profits and capital formation based on prospective profits are the lifeblood of capitalism. Dynamic growth in turn depends on capital formation. Governmental welfare spending has effects more like those of the foundations

which millionaires establish for welfare, religious, cultural, and tax-avoiding purposes than the effects of the essential supportive institutions of capitalism.

Heavy spending for welfare would entail a radical change in strategy in the conflict with the Soviet Union. In a socialist economy the political and economic overseers are one and they need consider only themselves and the underlying population. Capital investment is therefore limited only by the initially adverse effects on the standard of living. Since in practice countries resort to socialism only when the standard of living is low and the objective is to raise it, military spending is an out-and-out handicap to the economy, without any compensating features. Under capitalism, military spending likewise comes out of the hides of the consumers, but in respect to business investment the situation is quite different. To induce businessmen to invest, the government must see to it that the prospects for profit are good. Military spending keeps the standard of living below what it could be and also takes a sizable cut of corporation profits, but it does compensate for the chronic shortage of purchasing power which would otherwise manifest itself in unemployment and depression. The United States is well able to pay this price and still maintain an acceptable standard of living for the middle classes, together with the highest corporate profits on record, even after taxes. At the same time socialist competitors are drained of resources which they cannot afford to squander with the same prodigality, and socialist administrators are presented with some extra headaches. This advantage in the cold war the United States would be loath to sacrifice—although it should be noted that some highly placed industrialists—the late Ernest T. Weir, for example—have been and are perfectly willing to take their chances in a peaceful contest with communism or any other system.

These men would no doubt be opposed to a switch from military to welfare spending; what this group wants is a minimum of government spending of any kind. Yet, if spending there must be, American capitalist enterprise, confronted with the problem of vastly increased production through automation, could take the wind out of the sails of communism more effectively by switching preponderantly from armaments to welfare than by any other conceivable diplomatic, propagandistic, or military maneuvers. The dominant drive of our time is the desire of the common man, whether of the lower classes of the advanced industrial nations or those of the industrially retarded ones, for a "better" life, by which he means a higher material scale of living and greater economic security. Whatever the ultimate worth of this ideal, those who already live by it are scarcely in a position to criticize it. The realization of this goal calls not only for automation and increased production, but for peace—for peace above all. But if so, just as military governmental spending is now the last resort of the hard-pressed corporate entrepreneur, nonmilitary governmental spending may at some future juncture be the only recourse for the whole economy.

American foreign policy, based almost entirely on military aid to foreign countries, has not been conspicuously successful. Soviet foreign policy is in no better case. Neither of the two superpowers has reliable allies. Nor has anyone else. What Anatole France said of women, that they do not give themselves, they *lend* themselves, is even more true of states pursuing their real or fancied interests. It may be that neutralism will grow and the two blocs will disintegrate more or less synchronously, so that neither will at any time have an overwhelming preponderance of military power, other than nuclear military power, the use of which by either would entail suicidal risks. An *arriviste* aggressor armed with nuclear weapons might emerge, but he would still have to reckon with the stockpiles and technology of the nuclear pioneers. By all indications the Soviet Union will have its hands full without a big war. The United States may be left without an opponent big and

threatening enough to justify plausibly military prepara-
tions on a scale large enough to be economically effective,
once the automatic factories really get going.

The dim outline of an international situation in which
spending for welfare will be as much of an imperative as
military spending is now, cannot leave the foresighted
businessman unconcerned. An economic leader worthy of
the name does not preoccupy himself with the immediate
profits of his own business, important as these are. He
looks around him at other industries and economies and to
the more remote future. The elder Morgan was a great innovator and rationalizer because he thought in ten-year
terms. Almost all our big businessmen do that now, or at
least pretend to. Some of this is press-relations stuff, but
surely not all of it. The businessmen who look this far
ahead—and it's not very far, actually—must take into
account the possible confluence of automation-swollen
output and a shrinking cold war.

It need not daunt them. There will always be plenty of
scope for managerial talent. The first requisite of the successful administrator is ability to adjust himself to changing circumstances and not be too slow about it. And,
as Schopenhauer said, it is wise to anticipate compulsion
by self-control. Even if a welfare-oriented government is
a step toward what they dread, they must consider, for
themselves and their children, whether the costs and perils
of an economy leaning on thermonuclear militarism are
not greater than the distasteful features of the welfare
state.

If the hypothesis is wrong, if, instead, the cold war ends in a hot one, what's one more wrong hypothesis in a holocaust? But, wishful though it be, the forecast may turn out to be right. If so, the business planners had better catch up with it before it catches up with them. It might be their last chance.